A NEW CALCULUS

PART I

WITH CHAPTERS ON

CO-ORDINATE GEOMETRY
DIFFERENTIATION AND INTEGRATION
AS SUMMATION

BY

A. W. SIDDONS, K. S. SNELL

AND

J. B. MORGAN

Assistant Masters at Harrow School

CAMBRIDGE
AT THE UNIVERSITY PRESS
1950

PUBLISHED BY
THE SYNDICS OF THE CAMBRIDGE UNIVERSITY PRESS

London Office: Bentley House, N.W. 1
American Branch: New York

Agents for Canada, India, and Pakistan: Macmillan

Printed in Great Britain at the University Press, Cambridge
(Brooke Crutchley, University Printer)

J. M. Loughridge E.M.M. V, M.L.

6/10/54

A NEW CALCULUS

PART I

CONTENTS

PREFACE

This is the first of three parts of a Calculus written for students at school and in their first year at a University. The first part is a preliminary course suitable for boys and girls in their elementary mathematics, especially for those who may go no further with the subject. It enables them to see the methods and applications of both differentiation and integration with a minimum of manipulation. This has been achieved with the differentiation of only a few powers of x, the emphasis being placed on the many applications that can be made with this simple material to problems in algebra, geometry and kinematics. Since some geometrical ideas are essential, a chapter has been inserted giving the elements of Co-ordinate Geometry, and linking it up with the graphical work of Algebra.

Most of this part is taken from Siddons and Daltry's *Elementary Algebra*. We are greatly indebted to Mr Daltry for allowing it to be used in this way. It covers very adequately the work suggested in the 'Alternative Syllabus' for Certificate of Education examinations. Some teachers may feel that some of their non-specialist pupils, who will not go on to Part II of this book, might well carry the work a little further, and be introduced to the other fundamental principle of the calculus, namely, the idea of integration as the limit of a summation. For such pupils we have added to Part I the first two chapters, 7 and 8, of Part II. Part II gives a course that should be sufficient for the engineer or scientist at school. Part III goes on to a more complete course, filling in work for the physicist and engineer, and giving a course for the mathematical specialist that covers essential ideas and prepares him for a University course of Analysis.

The authors' thanks for permission to include questions from public examination papers are due to the Oxford and Cambridge Schools Examination Board and the Northern Universities Joint Matriculation Board.

A. W. S.
K. S. S.
J. B. M.

January 1950

TO THE READER

It is intended that all the Exercises in the text should be worked as the chapter is read.

In the Exercises, a single rule is used to mark off questions which most pupils should do; the double rule indicates a change in the type of question.

CHAPTER 1

INTRODUCTORY

Function

1·1. If we wish to indicate that one variable changes when another variable changes, we say that the first is a **function** of the second. Thus a boy's weight changes as his age changes, so we say his weight is a function of his age, though there is no mathematical expression that gives his weight in terms of his age.

In calculus we shall be concerned with expressions such as $2x$, $3x^2-2$, $\frac{1}{x}$, $\sqrt{(4+x^2)}$, $\sin x$. Each of these changes as x changes, and so each is a function of x.

Graphs

1·2. You have already seen that if a number y is given equal to an expression containing x, e.g. $y = \frac{1}{5}x^2-3$, you can make a table giving corresponding values of x and y, and hence draw a graph showing how y changes as x changes.

In such a graph, if the co-ordinates of the point P are (x, y), the y is called the **ordinate** of P and the x the **abscissa** of P.

It should be noted that

(i) any pair of values of x and y that satisfy the equation give a point on the graph,

(ii) the x and y of any point on the graph satisfy the equation.

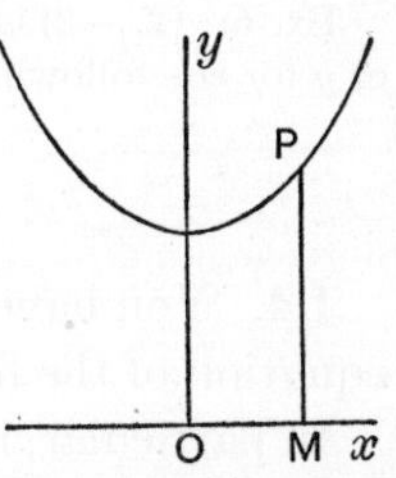

Fig. 1·1.

¶ Ex. 1. The curve in fig. 1·1 is the graph of $y = x^2+1$. Find the length of MP when OM has the values (i) 3, (ii) -2, (iii) a, (iv) $3+h$, (v) $a+h$.

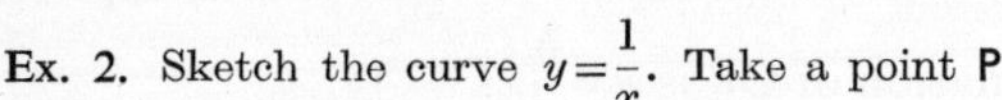
Ex. 2. Sketch the curve $y=\frac{1}{x}$. Take a point P on the curve and draw PM perpendicular to the x-axis. Find the length of MP when OM has the values given in Ex. 1.

Ex. 3. Repeat Ex. 2 for the curve $y = x(3-x)$.

¶ For discussion.

Increments

1·3. In figs. 1·2, 1·3, as you move from P to Q, MN or PR is called the increment of x and RQ is the corresponding increment of y.

Note that the increment of x in each figure is positive, and that the increment of y is positive in fig. 1·2 but negative in fig. 1·3.

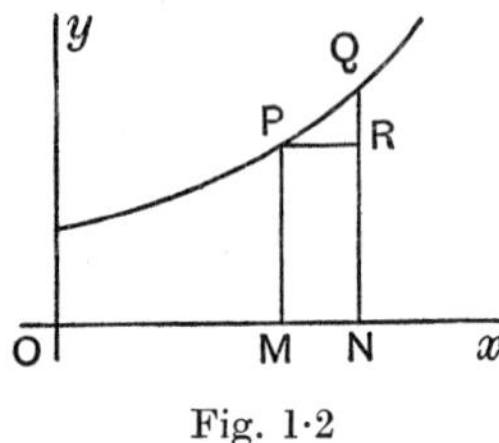

Fig. 1·2

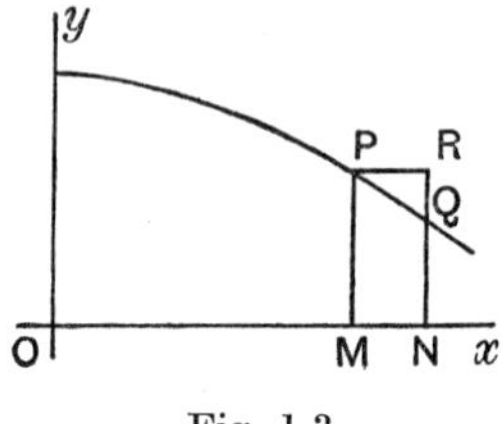

Fig. 1·3

Ex. 4. The radius of a circle is known to be 2 in. Find the error in the area of the circle if the radius is measured as (i) 2·1 in., (ii) $(2+h)$ in. [These give the increments of area corresponding to increments of 0·1 and h in. in the radius.]

Ex. 5. If a stone is falling freely, the distance it falls from rest in t sec. is given approximately by the equation $s=16t^2$. Find the distance fallen in 5 sec. and in the next $\frac{1}{2}$ sec. Also find the distance fallen in h sec. after the 5 sec. [These give the increments of distance corresponding to increments of $\frac{1}{2}$ sec. and h sec. in the time.]

Ex. 6. $(2, -2)$ is a point on the curve $y = 2-x^2$. What are the increments of y for the following increments of x: (i) 1, (ii) $\frac{1}{2}$, (iii) h?

The straight line

1·4. You have already seen that the graph corresponding to an equation of the first degree in x and y is a straight line.

In particular, in fig. 1·4 the equation of MP is $y=b$, the equation of NP is $x=a$, the equation of OP is $y=\frac{b}{a}x$.

In fig. 1·5 we have a straight line RQ which is not parallel to either axis and does not pass through the origin. The typical equation for such a line is

$$y = mx+c.$$

If Q is the point (x, y),

$$y = \mathsf{NQ} = \mathsf{NP} + \mathsf{PQ} = mx + c.$$

Note that m is the gradient of the line. See § 2·2.

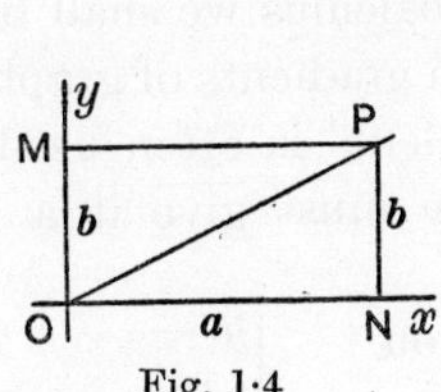

Fig. 1·4

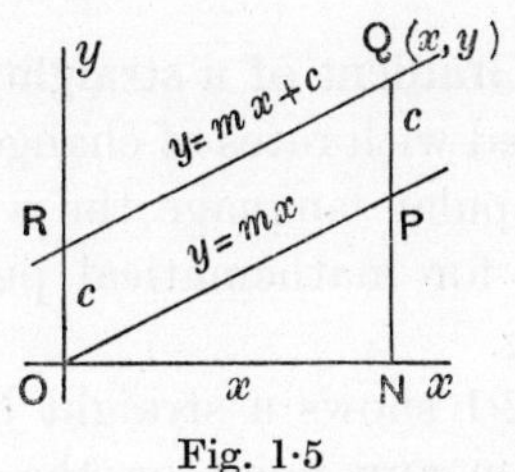

Fig. 1·5

Ex. 7. Make freehand sketches of the straight lines whose equations are (i) $y=2$, (ii) $y = -1$, (iii) $x=3$, (iv) $y = 3x+1$, (v) $y = -2x+2$, (vi) $2y+x = 4$, (vii) $x+y+2 = 0$.

CHAPTER 2

GRADIENT OF A GRAPH

2·1. Gradient of a straight line. In calculus we shall be much concerned with rates of change and with gradients of graphs.

In popular language the word 'gradient' is often used rather loosely; for mathematical purposes we must give it a definite meaning.

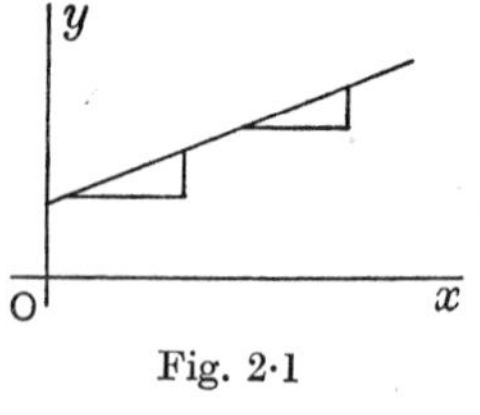

Fig. 2·1

Fig. 2·1 shows a straight line. As you pass from any point on the line to any other point on the line, the x and y of the point have corresponding increments; and by similar triangles we see that the fraction $\dfrac{\text{increment of } y}{\text{increment of } x}$ always has the same value whatever points are taken. Hence we have the following definition.

The **gradient** of a straight line is the fraction

$$\frac{\text{increment of } y}{\text{increment of } x},$$

where the increments are corresponding increments.

Note that in fig. 2·1 the corresponding increments of x and y are both positive or both negative, so that the gradient of the line is positive.

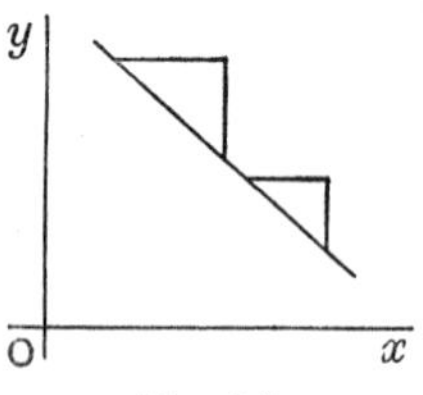

Fig. 2·2

In fig. 2·2 the corresponding increments of x and y are one positive and the other negative, so that the gradient of the line is negative.

2·2. Gradient of $y = mx + c$. In fig. 1·5 as you pass from O to P,

$$\frac{\text{increment of } y}{\text{increment of } x} = \frac{\text{NP}}{\text{ON}} = m.$$

$\therefore$ the gradient of OP is m.

RQ is parallel to OP.

$\therefore$ the gradient of RQ is m.

That is, the gradient of $y = mx + c$ is m.

2·3. Average gradient. Consider the case of an undulating road, or a curved graph. We cannot yet determine the gradient of a curve, as we have defined the term only for a straight line. But we can determine the **average** gradient over any length of the road, by calculating the gradient of a road of uniform slope that coincides with the actual road at the beginning and end of the length in question. Similarly, the average gradient of a curved graph between two points is the gradient of the chord joining these points.

Example 1. Find the gradient of the chord of $y=x^2$ which joins the points for which $x=2$ and $x=5$.

The two points are $(2, 4)$ $(5, 25)$.
The gradient of the chord

$$=\frac{\text{increment of } y}{\text{increment of } x}$$

$$=\frac{25-4}{5-2}=\frac{21}{3}=7.$$

So the gradient of the chord is 7, or the average gradient of the curve between $x=2$ and $x=5$ is 7.

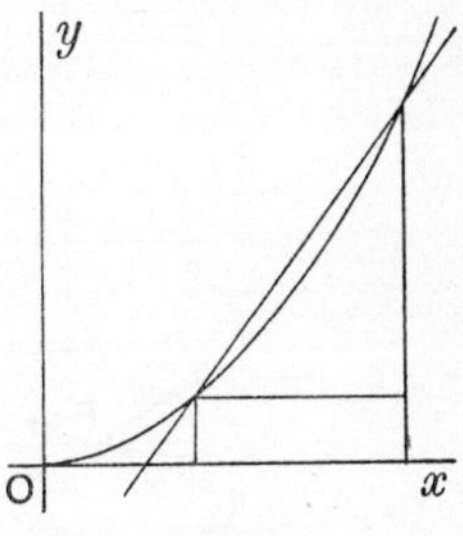

Fig. 2·3

Ex. 1. Find the average gradient of $y=x^2$ for the intervals

(i) $x=2$ to $x=4$, (ii) $x=1$ to $x=3$, (iii) $x=-2$ to $x=0$.

2·4. Tangent to a curve. If a sheet of flat metal, cut with its edge in the shape of any curve, is laid flat on a table, and a straight edge pressed against the curved edge at any point, the edge in contact with the curve is a tangent to the curve at this point (fig. 2·4).

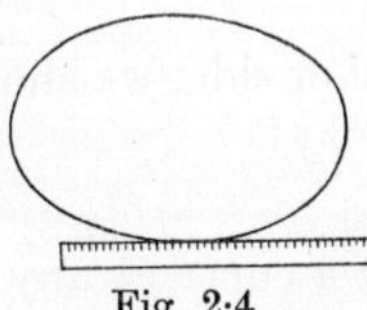
Fig. 2·4

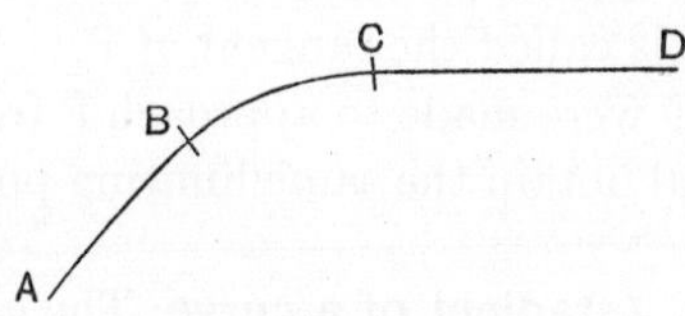

Fig. 2·5

We get an equally good notion of what 'tangent' means if we lay a piece of cotton along part of the curve, and pull it out straight from the point where it leaves the curve; the straight part of the cotton will be a tangent to the curve at this point. Again, the straight pieces AB, CD of the railway ABCD are tangents to the curve BC (fig. 2·5) at B and C respectively.

For mathematical purposes it is found useful to treat the idea of tangent in the following way.

Through a point P of a curve (fig. 2·6) draw the chord PQ, meeting the curve again at Q; produce this chord indefinitely, past Q.

Now let the point Q move along the curve towards P, through the positions Q_1, Q_2, Q_3, etc., carrying the chord with it. The chord

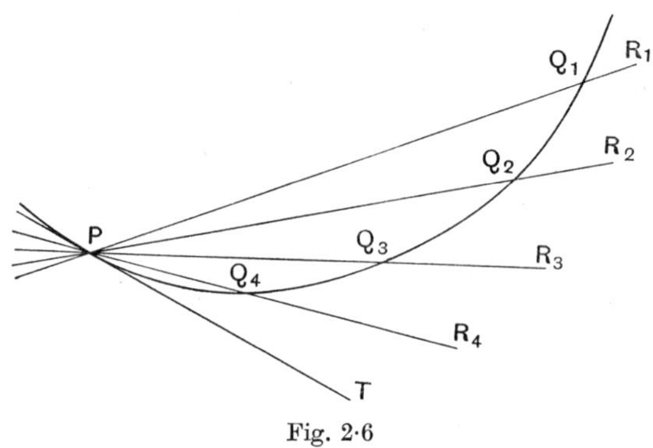

Fig. 2·6

revolves about P, and the portion PQ becomes shorter and shorter. Let us attend, however, to PR, the chord produced.

The closer Q comes to P, the more nearly does PR give the true direction of the curve at P. As Q approaches closer and closer to P, so does PR approach closer and closer to a limiting position PT, which is called the tangent at P,

If Q were made to approach P from the other side, we should in general obtain the same limiting position.

2·5. Gradient of a curve. The gradient of a curve at any point is defined to be the gradient of the tangent at this point.

We can find the gradient at any point of a curve approximately by drawing the tangent by eye (with the aid of a ruler) and measuring its gradient, but we must find a more precise method.

2·6. To find the gradient of the curve $y=x^2$ at the point (2, 4). We will first consider this arithmetically.

We have seen that the tangent PT (see fig. 2·6) is the limiting position to which a chord PQ approaches, as Q approaches closer and closer to P.

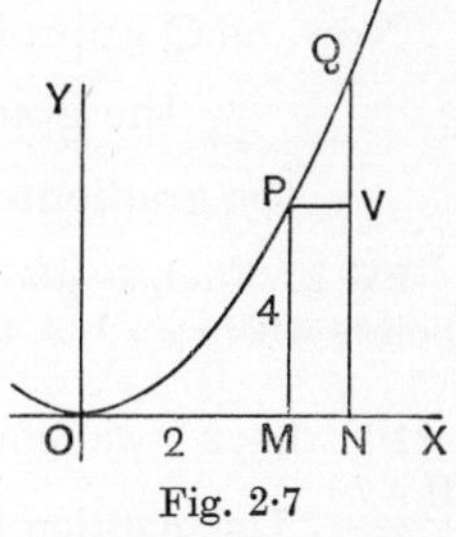

Fig. 2·7

The gradient of PQ is the average gradient of the curve between the points P and Q. As Q approaches P, so does the average gradient between P and Q approach closer and closer to the gradient of the curve *at* P.

Let us therefore first calculate the gradient of the chord PQ, for various positions of Q.

We have OM = 2. Let MN = 0·5, so that the x of Q is 2·5. Then the y of Q, namely,

$$NQ = 2{\cdot}5^2 = 6{\cdot}25.$$

$$\therefore\ VQ = 6{\cdot}25 - 4 = 2{\cdot}25.$$

$$\therefore \text{ the gradient of PQ} = \frac{VQ}{PV} = \frac{2{\cdot}25}{0{\cdot}5} = 4{\cdot}5.$$

Now take a succession of positions for Q, as it approaches P, the x's being 2·2, 2·1, 2·01.

If we tabulate these results, we have

ON	2·5	2·2	2·1	2·01
Gradient of PQ	4·5	4·2	4·1	4·01

We cannot take the last step and put ON = 2·0, for in that case the triangle QVP disappears. The successive gradients *suggest*, however, that the limiting value—the gradient of the tangent to the curve—is 4. We could test this further by taking ON = 2·001 or 2·00001, but in the next paragraph we will consider the matter algebraically and show that the limit is really 4.

2·7. In fig. 2·8, let PV $=h$, VQ $=k$. Then the co-ordinates of Q are $(2+h, 4+k)$. But Q is on the curve $y=x^2$.

$$\therefore\ 4+k = (2+h)^2$$

$$= 4+4h+h^2.$$

$$\therefore\ k = 4h+h^2.$$

∴ the gradient of PQ

$$= \frac{\mathsf{VQ}}{\mathsf{PV}} = \frac{k}{h} = \frac{4h+h^2}{h} = 4+h, \quad \text{if} \quad h \neq 0.$$

Now, as Q approaches P, so $h \to 0$.

∴ the gradient of PQ $\to 4$.

∴ the gradient of the curve at P is 4.

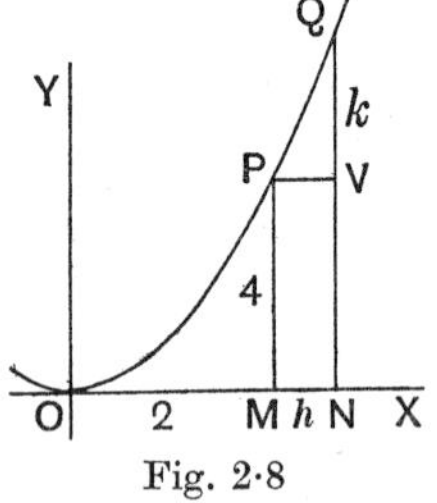

Fig. 2·8

Ex. 2. Find, as above, the gradient of $y=x^2$ at points where $x=1, 3, 4$.

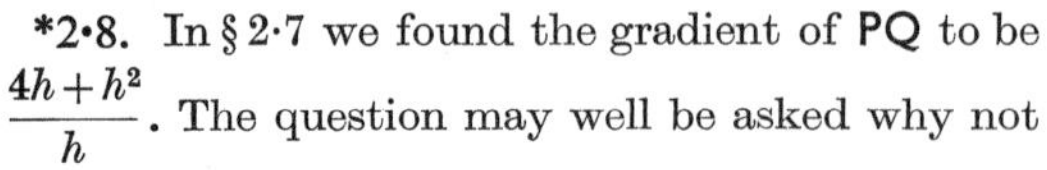
***2·8.** In § 2·7 we found the gradient of PQ to be $\dfrac{4h+h^2}{h}$. The question may well be asked why not put $h=0$ at once. If we do, we have nothing but the meaningless expression $\frac{0}{0}$.

It will be well to spend a little time in examining the meaning of the word 'limit'.

Consider an expression such as $\dfrac{4h+h^2}{h}$. This is a function of h, and its value can be found for any value of h except $h=0$. In fact, *unless* $h=0$, $\dfrac{4h+h^2}{h} \equiv 4+h$; and there is no difficulty. But if $h=0$, we have a fraction that looks like $\frac{0}{0}$. Now the process of division, as defined in arithmetic, does not contemplate 0 as a divisor. In fact, $\frac{0}{0}$ is an undefined and unmeaning combination, and when $h=0$, $\dfrac{4h+h^2}{h}$ cannot be evaluated.

But though we cannot find a value for the function $\dfrac{4h+h^2}{h}$ when $h=0$, we can find the limit to which the function tends as h tends towards 0; or, more briefly, as $h \to 0$. For $\dfrac{4h+h^2}{h} \equiv 4+h$, whatever value h may have, however small, provided that $h \neq 0$. Impress upon your mind that 0 is entirely different from a small number, however small. Thus, a small object can be magnified to any required size; but no amount of magnification will make 0 anything but 0.

As $h \to 0$, $4+h$ becomes more and more nearly equal to 4. We are inclined to say that the limit of $4+h$ as $h \to 0$ *is* 4; but first note the following remark about the word 'limit'. Before we can assert that 4 is the limit of $4+h$ as $h \to 0$, we must be prepared to satisfy a certain test. If one person (A) mentions any small number he cares to choose, another person (B) must be able by choosing h properly to make the difference between $4+h$ and the alleged limit numerically less than this small number. There must be no

* This may be omitted at first reading.

collusion between A and B. Thus, A mentions $\frac{1}{100{,}000}$; can B make the difference between $4+h$ and 4 numerically less than $\frac{1}{100{,}000}$? The difference is h; and B can succeed by taking h somewhat less than $\frac{1}{100{,}000}$; say $h=\frac{1}{100{,}001}$. Whatever small number A chooses, B can always meet him. This being so, we may say that, as $h \to 0$, so $\frac{4h+h^2}{h}$ tends to the limit 4; or $\frac{4h+h^2}{h} \to 4$.

This may seem unnecessarily troublesome; why not put $h=0$ straight away? Because if we put $h=0$, $\frac{4h+h^2}{h}$ becomes $\frac{0}{0}$ which is meaningless.

2·9. The gradient of $y=x^2$ at *any* point on the curve.

Let P, (x, y), be any point on the curve and Q, $(x+h, y+k)$, be a near point on the curve. (See fig. 2·9.)

As P is on the curve, $y=x^2$.

As Q is on the curve,

$$y+k = (x+h)^2 = x^2+2hx+h^2.$$

$$\therefore\ k = 2hx+h^2.$$

$\therefore$ the gradient of PQ

$$=\frac{k}{h}=\frac{2hx+h^2}{h} = 2x+h, \quad \text{if} \quad h \neq 0.$$

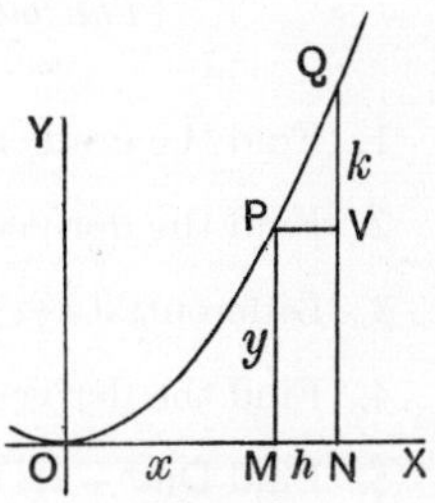

Fig. 2·9

Now, as Q approaches P,

$$h \to 0 \quad \text{and} \quad 2x+h \to 2x.$$

$\therefore$ the gradient of the curve at P $= 2x$.

2·10. If we want to calculate the *ordinate*—i.e. the distance up to the curve—for any value of x, we work out the value of x^2.

If we want to calculate the *gradient* for any value of x, we work out the value of $2x$.

Thus x^2 may be described as the expression for the ordinate; $2x$ as the expression for the gradient.

Or, in other words, the function x^2 gives the ordinate, and the function $2x$ the gradient, for any value of x.

x^2 is the original function that defines the curve; $2x$ is called the **derived function** of x^2, or the **gradient function** of x^2.

The process of finding the derived function of a given function is called **differentiation**: we are said to **differentiate** a function. The derived function of x^2 is written $\mathsf{D}x^2$; thus we have found that $\mathsf{D}x^2 = 2x$.* Note carefully that D is not a number or a multiplier; but simply an abbreviation for 'the derived function of'.

In the same way, the derived function of $2x^2$ is written $\mathsf{D}(2x^2)$; the derived function of $2x^2 - 3x + 5$ is written $\mathsf{D}(2x^2 - 3x + 5)$.

We may be considering a function of some variable other than x, say of t: thus $\mathsf{D}t^2 = 2t$.

If there is any ambiguity as to the variable with respect to which we are differentiating, we may use a suffix: thus the derived function of $2x^2 + t$ with respect to x may be written $\mathsf{D}_x(2x^2 + t)$. If only one variable occurs in the function to be differentiated, the suffix is not needed.

Exercise 2*a*

(The following differentiations are to be performed from first principles as in § 2·9)

1. Find the gradient of $y = 2x^2$. Compare this with the gradient of $y = x^2$.

2. Find the derived function of $5x^2$, and compare it with that of x^2.

3. Differentiate $\frac{1}{2}x^2$, and compare the result with that of differentiating x^2.

4. Find the derived function of ax^2, a being a constant number.

5. Find $\mathsf{D}(x^2 + 2)$; $\mathsf{D}_x(x^2 + c)$; $\mathsf{D}_x(ax^2 + c)$.

2·11. To differentiate a constant. This is the same as to find the gradient of $y = c$, where c is a constant. Now $y = c$ is a straight line parallel to the x-axis and c units above it. Its gradient is therefore zero. Therefore the result of differentiating a constant is zero; in other words, the derived function of a constant is zero, i.e. $\mathsf{D}_x c = 0$.

2·12. To differentiate the function $mx + c$. This is equivalent to finding the gradient of $y = mx + c$. In § 2·2 this has been shown to be m.

$$\therefore\ \mathsf{D}_x(mx + c) = m.$$

Or as follows. Let $y = mx + c$; and suppose that when x is in-

* Strictly $\mathsf{D}x^2 \equiv 2x$.

creased to $x+h$, y is increased to $y+k$. Since $(x+h, y+k)$ is a point on the graph

$$y+k = m(x+h)+c$$
$$= mx+mh+c.$$
$$\therefore\ k = mh.$$
$$\therefore\ \frac{k}{h} = m, \quad \text{a constant.}$$
$$\therefore\ \mathsf{D}_x(mx+c) = m.$$

Ex. 3. Read off the derived functions of

$$x, \quad 2x, \quad \tfrac{1}{2}x, \quad 3x-2, \quad 3x-5, \quad 4-3x, \quad a+bx.$$

2·13. To differentiate ax^2+bx+c.

Let $y = ax^2+bx+c$, and suppose that, when x is increased to $x+h$, y is increased to $y+k$.

Since $(x+h, y+k)$ is a point on the graph

$$y+k = a(x+h)^2 \quad +b(x+h)+c.$$
$$\therefore\ y+k = a(x^2+2xh+h^2)+b(x+h)+c.$$

Since (x, y) is a point on the graph

$$y = ax^2 \quad +bx \quad +c.$$
$$\therefore \quad k = a(2xh+h^2) \quad +bh.$$
$$\therefore \quad \frac{k}{h} = a(2x+h) \quad +b.$$

Now as $h \to 0$ $\quad \frac{k}{h} \to a\,.\,2x \quad +b.$

$$\therefore\ \mathsf{D}_x(ax^2+bx+c) = 2ax\ +b.$$

Note that, if b and c are each 0 (or if you cover up the columns that contain b and c), the above work shows the differentiation of ax^2; similarly if a and c are each 0, we have the differentiation of bx and so on.

Hence we see that the derived function of the sum of several terms is the sum of the derived functions of the separate terms.

Also we see that the derived function of ax^2 is a times the derived function of x^2.

Example 2. Differentiate $2x^2-3x+\frac{1}{2}$.

$$\begin{aligned}\mathsf{D}(2x^2-3x+\tfrac{1}{2}) \\ &= \mathsf{D}(2x^2)-\mathsf{D}(3x)+\mathsf{D}(\tfrac{1}{2}) \\ &= 2\times 2x-3\times 1+0 \\ &= 4x-3.\end{aligned}$$

With a little practice, such differentiations may be performed in one line.

Exercise 2*b*

1. Read off the derived functions of the following functions:

(i) x^2+5, (ii) x^2+3x-1, (iii) $3x^2+x+2$,

(iv) $\frac{1}{2}x-\frac{3}{4}x^2$, (v) $3-\frac{4}{3}x^2+4x$, (vi) ax^2+bx+c.

2. What is the geometrical meaning of the fact that $3x^2+x-1$ and $3x^2+x+2$ have the same derived function?

3. If $y=x(3-x)$, what is $\mathsf{D}_x y$? Tabulate the values of y and of $\mathsf{D}_x y$ for $x=0, 1, 2, 3$. On inch paper mark the points found and at each point (by aid of the gradient) draw the tangent. Do not draw the curve, but note how the tangents would help in drawing it.

4. Find the gradients of the graph of $y=5x-\dfrac{x^2}{6}$ at $x=2$ and $x=16$.

---

5. Show that the gradient of the graph of $y=1+2x+2x^2$ at the point $(4, 41)$ is three times the gradient at the point $(1, 5)$.

6. Show that the gradient at the point (2, 4) of the curve

$$y=-1+3x-\frac{x^2}{4}$$

is double that at the point (4, 7); find the point on the curve at which the gradient is -1.

7. Find the gradients of the tangents to the curve $9y=x^2+4x+13$ at the points where it cuts the line $y=2$, and prove that the two tangents and the y-axis form an isosceles triangle.

2·14. To find the greatest or least values of a quadratic expression.

You have probably found these by algebraic processes,* but the use of gradient functions gives a method that can be applied later to expressions of higher degree.

* See Siddons and Daltry's *Algebra*, p. 368, nos. 56–58.

You have already seen that the graph of

$$y = ax^2 + bx + c$$

is always a parabola with its axis vertical (see fig. 2·10). Consider the sign of the gradient of each of these curves in turn as x increases from 0. When the gradient of the curve is 0 what can you say about the value of y?

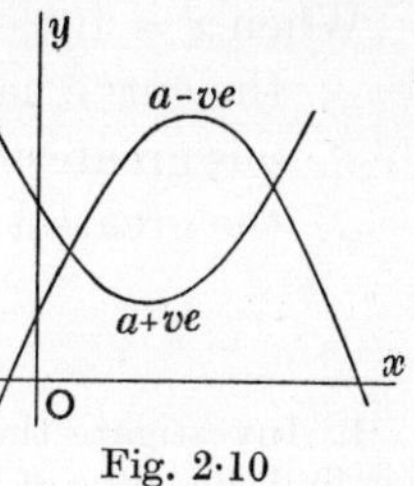

Fig. 2·10

Example 3. To find the greatest or least values of $2x^2 - 3x + 1$.

Let $y = 2x^2 - 3x + 1$. The gradient or derived function is $4x - 3$, or in symbols $\mathsf{D}y = \mathsf{D}(2x^2 - 3x + 1) = 4x - 3 = 4(x - \frac{3}{4})$.

Now $\mathsf{D}y = 0$ when $x = \frac{3}{4}$.

$\therefore$ when $x = \frac{3}{4}$, the value of y is greatest or least.

When $x = \frac{3}{4}$, $y = 2(\frac{3}{4})^2 - 3(\frac{3}{4}) + 1 = -\frac{1}{8}$.

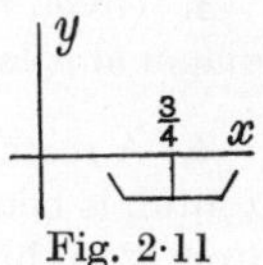

Fig. 2·11

To ascertain whether this value of y is greatest or least we must consider the sign of the gradient on each side of $x = \frac{3}{4}$. We shall use $x = \frac{3}{4}+$ to denote that x is a little larger than $\frac{3}{4}$ and $x = \frac{3}{4}-$ to denote that x is a little less than $\frac{3}{4}$.

When $x = \frac{3}{4}+$, $\mathsf{D}y$ [i.e. $4(x - \frac{3}{4})$] is positive.

When $x = \frac{3}{4}-$, $\mathsf{D}y$ is negative.

$\therefore$ the curve has to fit into a figure like fig. 2·11.

$\therefore$ when $x = \frac{3}{4}$, the value of y is least.

$\therefore$ the least value of y is $-\frac{1}{8}$ and it occurs when $x = \frac{3}{4}$.

Example 4. What is the greatest rectangular area that can be enclosed by 200 hurdles each 2 yd. long?

The total perimeter of the rectangle is 400 yd.

Suppose that one side is x yd.; then the other side is $(200 - x)$ yd.; and the area is $x(200 - x)$ sq.yd.

Let $y = x(200 - x)$. Then we want to find the value of x that makes y greatest.

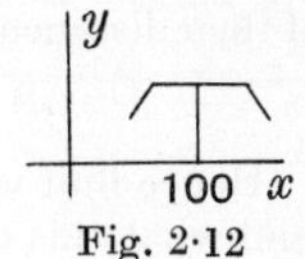

Fig. 2·12

$$\mathsf{D}y = \mathsf{D}(200x - x^2) = 200 - 2x = 2(100 - x).$$

$\therefore$ $\mathsf{D}y = 0$ when $x = 100$.

$\therefore$ when $x = 100$, y is greatest or least.

When $x = 100+$, $\mathsf{D}y$ is negative.

When $x = 100-$, Dy is positive.

$\therefore$ the curve has to fit into a figure like fig. 2·12.

$\therefore$ y is greatest when $x = 100$.

$\therefore$ the greatest area is $100(200-100) = 10{,}000$ sq.yd.

Exercise 2*c*

1. Investigate the greatest or least values of the following expressions, i.e. find the value of x for which the expressions are greatest or least, find the value of the expressions for the particular value of x and determine whether it is a greatest or a least value:

(i) $2-3x^2+6x$, (ii) $\frac{1}{2}x^2-2x-7$, (iii) $(x-1)(x-3)$.

2. Divide 10 into two parts such that (i) their product is greatest, (ii) the sum of their squares is least.

3. Given that the perimeter of a rectangle is $2p$, find for what shape the diagonal is least. (If the diagonal is least, so also is its square.)

4. A rectangular channel pipe, open at the top, sides vertical, base horizontal, is bent up out of a long piece of thin sheet iron 12 in. broad, so that, x in. being the base and y in. the depth of the channel, $2y+x = 12$ (see fig. 2·13). What is the area of the cross-section of the channel? For what value of x will it be greatest? (Eliminate y from the function that expresses the area.)

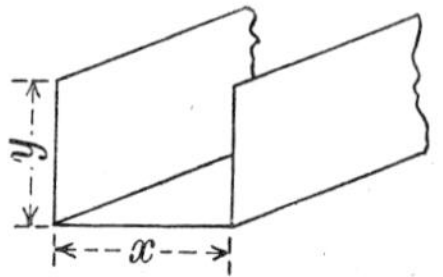

Fig. 2·13

5. If a stone is projected with velocity 64 ft. per sec. in a direction making an angle 30° with the horizon, its height in feet after t sec. is $32t-16t^2$. Find the value of t for which this is greatest, and hence find the greatest height reached by the stone.

6. In fig. 2·14, find the least length for PQ.

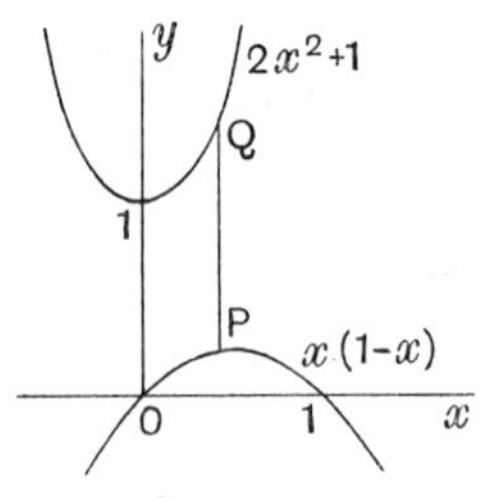

Fig. 2·14

7. A and B start walking at noon towards a point O. A starts at P, 9 miles due South of O, and B starts at Q, 13 miles due West of O. A walks 4 miles an hour, and B 3 miles an hour. Show that if their distance apart after x hours is d miles, then

$$d^2 = 25x^2-150x+250.$$

Hence find when their distance apart is least, and what this distance is. (Find when d^2 is least.)

---

8. Investigate the greatest or least values of the following expressions, i.e. find the value of x for which the expressions are greatest or least, find the value of the expressions for the particular value of x and determine whether it is a greatest or a least value:

(i) $12x-2-3x^2$, (ii) $2x(3-x)$, (iii) $(x+1)^2+(x+3)^2$.

9. In fig. 2·15, find the greatest length for RS.

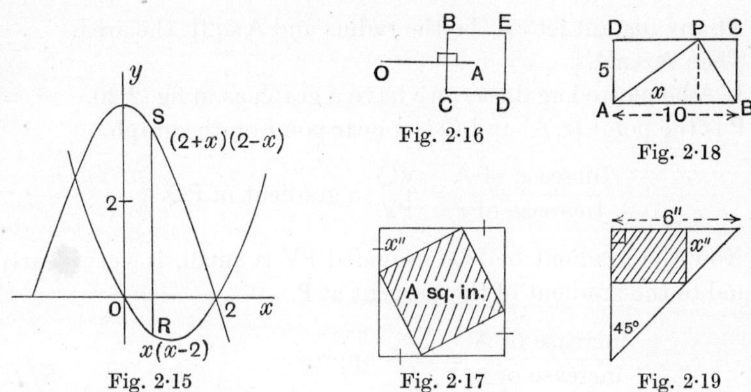

Fig. 2·15 Fig. 2·16 Fig. 2·17 Fig. 2·18 Fig. 2·19

10. In fig. 2·16, OA is 4 in. and A is the centre of the square BCDE whose sides are $2x$ in. long. Find an expression for OB^2 in terms of x. Hence find the least length of OB. (Find when OB^2 is least.)

11. Fig. 2·17 shows a square inscribed in a square of side 2 in. Prove that the area, A sq.in., of the inscribed square is given by $A = 2x^2-4x+4$.
Find the value of x which makes A least.

12. In fig. 2·18, find the value of x that makes PA^2+PB^2 least.

13. In fig. 2·19, find the greatest area the shaded rectangle can have.

14. A piece of wire of length l is cut into two portions of lengths x and $(l-x)$. Each portion is then cut into twelve equal parts which are soldered together so as to form the edges of a cube. Find an expression for the sum of the volumes of the two cubes so formed.
What is the least value of the sum of the volumes?

15. A piece of wire, which forms the circumference of a circle of 12 in. radius, is cut and bent so as to form two new circles. Find the radius of each circle in order that the sum of the areas of the two circles may be as small as possible.

Small increases*

2·15. Example 5. A circular metal plate, of radius 2 ft., expands on rise of temperature to radius 2·003 ft. Find approximately the increase of area.

At any instant let r ft. be the radius and A sq.ft. the area.
Then $A = \pi r^2$.
If A be plotted against r, we have a graph as in fig. 2·20.
P is the point (r, A) and Q is a near point on the graph.

$$\frac{\text{Increase of A}}{\text{Increase of } r} = \frac{VQ}{PV} = \text{gradient of PQ.}$$

Now the gradient of PQ, provided PV is small, is very nearly equal to the gradient of the tangent at P.

$$\therefore \frac{\text{increase of A}}{\text{increase of } r} = D_r A \text{ approx.}$$

$$= 2\pi r \text{ approx.}$$

$\therefore$ increase of A is approximately $2\pi r \times$ increase in r

$$= 2\pi \times 2 \times 0{\cdot}003$$

$$= \pi \times 0{\cdot}012.$$

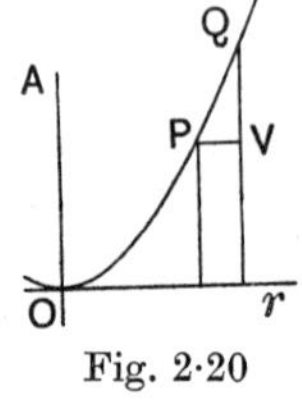

Fig. 2·20

$\therefore$ increase of area $= 0{\cdot}038$ sq.ft. to two significant figures.

Exercise 2*d*

1. The surface area of a sphere of radius r is $4\pi r^2$. If the radius of a sphere increases from 10 to 10·1 cm., find the approximate increase in surface area.

2. If a copper bar is 1 ft. long at 0° C., the length (l ft.) at θ° C. is given by the formula $l = 1 + a\theta + b\theta^2$, where

$$a = 0{\cdot}1607 \times 10^{-4}, \quad b = 0{\cdot}004 \times 10^{-6}.$$

Find an approximate value for the expansion between 10° C. and 11° C.

3. The distance of the visible horizon (x miles) as seen from a height of y ft. above sea-level is given by the formula $1{\cdot}5y = x^2$. To what height is it necessary to ascend in order to see 15 miles? Approximately how much higher must one climb to see an additional $\frac{1}{4}$ mile?

* May be omitted at a first reading.

4. A cylinder of length 10 in. and *diameter* $2\frac{3}{16}$ in. is turned down to diameter $2\frac{1}{8}$ in. Calculate approximately (to two significant figures) the diminution of volume: and find by how much per cent. the volume is diminished (percentage to one significant figure).

5. If the radius of a metal sphere increases 1 % on a rise of temperature, prove that the surface increases approximately 2 %.

CHAPTER 3

RATE OF CHANGE

3·1. If a stone is let fall from a high tower, or down a pit shaft, let us suppose that it falls s ft. in t sec. from rest, i.e. from the instant it is let fall. If distances and times are observed, it will be found that the formula $s=16t^2$ very closely represents the observations.

Everyone will agree that the stone moves slowly at first and more and more rapidly as time goes on, but when it is asked, *exactly how fast* is the stone falling after 1 sec., or after 2 sec., the meaning of the question is not so obvious.

We know that the **average velocity** of a moving body during a certain interval of time is measured by

$$\frac{\text{No. of units of length traversed}}{\text{No. of units of time in interval}}.$$

Ex. 1. Using the formula $s=16t^2$, find the distance fallen from rest by a stone in 1, $1\frac{1}{2}$, 2, 3, 4 sec.

Hence find the distance traversed and the average velocity, in feet per second, during the following intervals of time after the start:

(i) 1 sec. to 4 sec., (ii) 1 sec. to 3 sec.,

(iii) 1 sec. to 2 sec., (iv) 1 sec. to $1\frac{1}{2}$ sec.

Ex. 2. Repeat Ex. 1 for the interval 1 sec. to $(1+h)$ sec. and use your result to check your answers to Ex. 1.

3·2. If we plot the graph $s=16t^2$, taking t across the page and s up the page (in fact, taking t for x and s for y), this graph is called a **time-space** graph. Of what shape is the time-space graph in this case?

The average velocity over an interval of time is measured by the ratio $\dfrac{\text{change of } s}{\text{change of } t}$. This ratio may also be called the **average rate of change** of s. Notice now that this ratio is exactly the same as that which gives the average gradient of the graph. The average velocity, or the average rate of change of s, is represented graphically by the average gradient of the graph.

3·3. We can now return to the question what is meant by the velocity of the falling stone *at* a certain instant. We might perhaps be tempted to define it as the average velocity over a small interval of time, beginning or ending at the specified instant. But would the average velocity be the same in both cases, and how small is the interval to be?

Now consider the following definition: **The velocity at a certain instant is the limit of the average velocity during an interval beginning at the specified instant, as the interval tends to zero.**

We have already seen that the limit of the average gradient is measured precisely by the derived function. In just the same way, the limit of the average velocity is measured by the derived function. In the present case, the velocity at the instant t is measured precisely by $D_t(16t^2)$ (remember that t now takes the place of x). What is $D_t(16t^2)$? What is the velocity after 1 sec.? How does this compare with the series of average velocities obtained in Exx. 1, 2?

Just as the average velocity is represented graphically by the average gradient in the time-space graph, so the velocity at a certain instant is represented graphically by the gradient of the time-space graph at the corresponding point.

Exercise 3*a*

Graphical

1. Fig. 3·1 is the time-space graph of a train starting from rest. Find the average velocities (i) during the 1st minute, (ii) during the 2nd minute, (iii) during the first 2 minutes.

Also find the velocity at the end of the first minute.

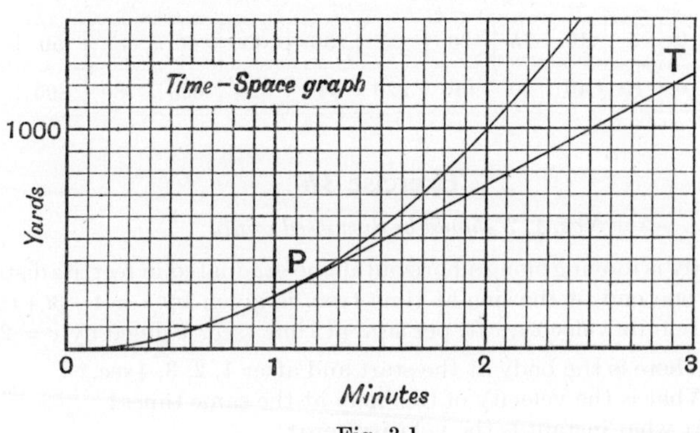

Fig. 3·1

2. The elevation of an aeroplane is observed every second and found to be as follows:

Second	0	1	2	3	4	5	6
Elevation	40°	45°	$51\frac{1}{2}$°	59°	68°	$78\frac{1}{2}$°	90°

At what rate is the elevation increasing at 1 sec. and at 3 sec.?

3. The following table gives observations of the Centigrade temperature of some water in a vessel.

The temperature taken at intervals of 5 min. was:

80°, 67°, 56°, 47°, 40°, 35°, 31°.

Plot the temperatures against the times and join by a smooth curve.

Estimate, as nearly as you can, the rate at which the temperature was falling at the instant when the temperature was 60°, and when it was 50°, and when it was 40°.

---

4. The amount of water in a tank at various times after opening a tap is given in the following table:

Time in seconds	0	5	10	15	20	30	40	50	55	60	70
Amount of water in gallons	64	56·2	49	42·3	36	25	16	9	6·25	4	1

Plot these quantities and deduce from the curve the rate at which water was leaving the tank at the end of 15 and 55 sec.

5. A train, starting from rest, moves a distance of 800 yd. in 50 sec., and the table below gives corresponding values of distance x in yards and time t in seconds. Plot the time-space graph, and deduce from it the velocities at 0, 10, 20, 30, 35, 40, 50 sec., hence plot the time-velocity graph:

t	0	5	10	15	20	25	30	35	40	45	50
x	0	10	40	80	140	220	340	520	690	780	800

Exercise 3*b*

Nos. 1, 2 *should be discussed orally*

1. A body is moving along a horizontal line graduated in feet, its distance, s ft., from one end of the line at time t sec. is given by $s = 4-3t+t^2$. By differentiation its velocity, v ft. per sec., at time t sec. is given by $v = 2t-3$.

(i) Where is the body at the start and after 1, 2, 3, 4 sec.?

(ii) What is the velocity of the body at the same times?

(iii) At what instant is the velocity zero?

(iv) Where was the body at this instant?

(v) When is the velocity positive and when negative?

(vi) When the velocity was zero was the body at its greatest or its least distance from the origin?

2. Repeat No. 1 for $s = 2t^2 - 10t + 5$.

3. A point moves along the line OX so that its distance from O at any time is $(t^2 - 12t)$ ft. Find an expression for its velocity at this time. When is the body at rest? Sketch graphs showing the distance and velocity as functions of the time from $t = -3$ to $t = +5$.

4. A man 6 ft. high is walking at v ft. per sec. directly away from a lamp-post, the light being 10 ft. above the ground. Find (i) the velocity of the end of his shadow, (ii) the rate at which his shadow is growing.

(At t sec. after he passes the lamp-post, he is vt ft. from the post. Let distance of end of shadow from post be x ft., length of shadow y ft. Prove that $\frac{x}{10} = \frac{y}{6} = \frac{vt}{4}$; hence that velocity of end of shadow : rate of growth of shadow : velocity of man $= 5:3:2$.)

3·4. It should now be clear that, if we have an (x, y) graph, the gradient $(\mathsf{D}_x y)$ of the graph at any point can be regarded as the rate at which y is changing with respect to x for that value of x.

For example in a time-space graph the gradient at any point $(\mathsf{D}_t s)$ gives us the rate of change of the distance at time t, this we call the velocity at that time.

Similarly, if we draw a time-velocity graph the gradient at any point $(\mathsf{D}_t v)$ gives us the rate of change of the velocity at time t, this we call the acceleration at that time.

Thus in the case of the falling stone of §3·1. Let the distance fallen in t sec. be s ft.; the velocity attained in t sec. be v ft. per sec.; the acceleration at t sec. by a ft. per sec. per sec. Then

$$s = 16t^2,$$

$$v = \mathsf{D}_t s = \mathsf{D}(16t^2) = 32t,$$

$$a = \mathsf{D}_t v = \mathsf{D}(32t) = 32.$$

We see therefore that in the particular case of a falling stone the acceleration is constant. (Actually this is not quite true, as the resistance of the air comes into play; in fact the formula $s = 16t^2$ is not quite true for a stone falling *through the air*.)

Exercise 3c

1. The speed of a train is increased as follows:

Time in sec. from start	0	4	8	12	16	20	24
Velocity in ft. per sec.	0	1·4	3·6	6·3	9·4	12·4	13

Draw the time-velocity graph, and from it determine the acceleration of the train 12 sec. after the start.

2. A body starts from rest and moves in a straight line so that its velocity after t sec. is given by $v = 6t - 4t^2$. Find (i) the acceleration after 4 sec., (ii) the average acceleration during the 4th second.

3. A body moves in a straight line; and s, the number of feet from a fixed point after t sec., is given by the formula $s = \frac{3}{2} - 2t + \frac{1}{2}t^2$.

(i) How far is the body from the fixed point at the instant from which time is reckoned?

(ii) What is the velocity after t sec.?

(iii) Sketch the time-velocity graph.

(iv) What is the velocity when $t=0$? What is the meaning of its negative sign?

(v) When does the body begin to move in a positive direction?

(vi) When does the body pass through the origin? Account for the double answer.

(vii) What is the acceleration at the start? after 5 sec.?

4. In a straight-line motion the distance s ft. from the origin of the moving body at t sec. from the start is given by $s = 8 - 7t + t^2$. Find the velocity after 3 sec. and the average velocity during the fourth second. Find also the acceleration after 3 sec.

---

5. In a straight-line motion the velocity after t sec. is given by

$$v = 4 - 6t + 3t^2.$$

Find (i) the initial velocity, (ii) the initial acceleration, (iii) the acceleration after 2 sec., (iv) the average acceleration during the 2nd second.

6. A ball is thrown straight up into the air; and h, its height in feet after t sec., is given by the equation $h = 100t - 16t^2$. Find its velocity when $t=2$ and when $t=4$, and the acceleration when $t=3$.

Ratio of rates of change

3·5. Suppose that a beam of light is thrown through a square aperture on to a screen, making a square patch of light on the screen. The distance between the lantern and screen is varied, the size of the square patch of light varying accordingly. When the side of the square is x in. and is increasing at the rate of 2 in. per sec., at what rate is the area increasing?

At time t sec., let x in. be the side of the square, y sq.in. the area. Then $y=x^2$.

We are told $\mathsf{D}_t x=2$; what is $\mathsf{D}_t y$?

Suppose that τ, h, k are corresponding increments of t, x, y. Then the limits as $\tau \to 0$ of $\frac{h}{\tau}, \frac{k}{\tau}, \frac{k}{h}$ are $\mathsf{D}_t x$, $\mathsf{D}_t y$, $\mathsf{D}_x y$.

We shall assume that $\lim \text{ of } \frac{k}{h} = \lim \text{ of } \frac{\frac{k}{\tau}}{\frac{h}{\tau}} = \frac{\lim \text{ of } \frac{k}{\tau}}{\lim \text{ of } \frac{h}{\tau}}$.

Hence $$\mathsf{D}_x y = \frac{\mathsf{D}_t y}{\mathsf{D}_t x}.$$

Now $\mathsf{D}_x y=2x$ and $\mathsf{D}_t x=2$.

$$\therefore \; \mathsf{D}_t y = 4x.$$

$\therefore$ the area is increasing at the rate of $4x$ sq.in. per sec. For example, if the side of the square is 12 in., the area is increasing at the rate of 48 sq.in. per sec.

Note that while the side increases uniformly, the area increases faster and faster.

In general, if y is a function of x,

$$\frac{\text{Rate of change of } y}{\text{Rate of change of } x} = \mathsf{D}_x y.$$

If y be plotted against x, the ratio of the rates is given by the gradient of the graph. Accordingly we may look upon the gradient as giving the rate of change of y compared with that of x, which is sometimes called the x-rate of change of y.

Example 1. The radius of a sphere is expanding at the rate of 0·2 in. per min. At what rate is its surface area increasing when the radius is 10 in.?

Let A sq.in. be the surface area when the radius is r in.

Then $$\mathsf{A} = 4\pi r^2.$$

Take 1 in. and 1 min. as units of length and time.

We are given $\mathsf{D}_t r=0{\cdot}2$; we want to find $\mathsf{D}_t \mathsf{A}$.

$$\mathsf{A}=4\pi r^2. \quad \therefore \; \mathsf{D}_r \mathsf{A}=8\pi r.$$

Now
$$\frac{D_t A}{D_t r} = D_r A.$$

$$\therefore \frac{D_t A}{0{\cdot}2} = 8\pi r.$$

$$\therefore D_t A = \tfrac{16}{10}\pi r.$$

∴ when $r=10$, the area is increasing at the rate of 16π sq.in. per min.

Exercise 3*d*

1. The radius of a circle increases uniformly at the rate of 0·1 in. per sec. At what rate is the area increasing when the radius is 1 ft.?

2. A spherical soap bubble is expanding, the radius increasing at the rate of a in. per sec. At what rate is the surface of the soap bubble increasing when the radius is 6 in.? 9 in.? (Surface$=4\pi r^2$.)

3. A pianola record, in the form of a long strip of paper a in. wide, is being wound on to a cylinder a in. long at the rate of b cu.in. per sec. At what rate is the radius of the roll increasing when the radius is x in.?

4. Find where the x and the y of the curve $y = 5x-x^2$ are increasing at the same rate; and also where y is increasing twice as fast as x.

5. The position of a moving point, at time t, referred to a pair of axes is given by the equations $x = 80t$, $y = 60t-16t^2$.

By eliminating t find the equation of the path.

Find $D_t x$, $D_t y$, $D_x y$ and calculate the values of these and of x and y when $t=2$. Verify that, when $t=2$, $D_x y = D_t y/D_t x$.

For what value of t is $D_t y=0$? What is the corresponding value of x?

---

6. Repeat No. 5 for $x = 20t$, $y = 24t-16t^2$.

7. A V-shaped drinking trough is 3 ft. long, and its vertical cross-section is a right-angled isosceles triangle. Prove that when the depth of the water is x in., the volume of water in the trough is $36x^2$ cu.in. If water is flowing in at the rate of 1000 cu.in. per min., at what rate is the surface rising when the depth is 6 in.? 10 in.?

Also find at what rate the surface is rising when the volume of water is 900 cu.in., and after 4 min. from starting to fill the trough.

8. A projectile is moving along a path whose equation is

$$y = \frac{x}{20} - \frac{x^2}{62500},$$

the unit of length being 1 ft. and the gun being at the origin; $D_t x$ is uniformly 1000 ft. per sec.: find $D_t y$ as a function of x. Also find at what horizontal distance the particle ceases to rise.

CHAPTER 4

FURTHER EXAMPLES OF DERIVED FUNCTIONS

4·1. So far we have only considered the derived functions of expressions such as ax^2+bx+c. We will now go on to consider the derived functions of more complicated expressions, but we will first introduce some new notation.

Functional notation

4·2. Any expression which involves x may be spoken of as a function of x and may be denoted by $f(x)$.

Note that $f(x)$ does not mean anything like a product of f and x, and that f is not a number; $f(x)$ is simply an abbreviation for a 'function of x'. Thus $3x^2+4$, $\sin x$, 10^x, $\log x$ are all functions of x.

Example 1. Evaluate $f(2)$ when (i) $f(x) \equiv 3x^2+4$, (ii) $f(x) \equiv 10^x$.

(i) $f(x) \equiv 3x^2+4$, $\quad \therefore\ f(2) = 3\times 2^2+4 = 12+4 = 16.$

(ii) $f(x) \equiv 10^x$, $\quad \therefore\ f(2) = 10^2 = 100.$

Exercise 4*a*

1. If $f(x) \equiv x^2+6x+7$, calculate $f(1), f(2), f(0), f(10)$.

2. If $f(x) \equiv \dfrac{10}{x+2}$, calculate $f(3), f(8), f(0), f(2)$.

3. If $f(x) \equiv (2x+1)(2x-1)-(x-1)$, find $f(x+1)$ in its simplest form.

4. If $f(x) \equiv x^3+3x^2+7x+1$, find $f(-x)$.

---

5. If $f(x) \equiv 2x^2-x-1$, find $f(x+1)$ and solve the equation $f(x+1) = 0$.

6. If $f(x) \equiv x^3-6x^2+12x-16$, find $f(x+2)$ and solve the equation $f(x+2) = 0$.

7. If $f(x) \equiv x^2+3x+4$, find $f(x+h)$.

Delta notation

4·3. In § 2·9 we considered a point (x, y) on the curve $y = x^2$ and a near point $(x+h, y+k)$ on the curve; the h was an extra piece of x, an increment of x, the k was an increment of y. It is convenient to use Δx (this is read 'delta x')* for h, thus Δx means 'the increment of x'; then Δy means 'the increment of y' corresponding to Δx.

The symbol Δ is not a number or a multiplier of x or y; Δx must be regarded as a number, just as x is a number. Thus $\dfrac{\Delta y}{\Delta x}$ is merely shorthand for $\dfrac{\text{increment of } y}{\text{increment of } x}$; it is what we wrote before as $\dfrac{k}{h}$ and measures the gradient of the line joining the points (x, y) and $(x+\Delta x, y+\Delta y)$.

N.B. $x\Delta x$ cannot be simplified; it is not equal to Δx^2. Δx^2 is dangerous; does it mean $(\Delta x)^2$ or $\Delta(x^2)$?

Exercise 4*b*

1. If $f(x) \equiv 3x^2 + 11$, what are $f(2), f(a), f(x+\Delta x)$?
2. If $f(t) \equiv 2t^2 - 7t + 5$, simplify $f(t+\Delta t)$.
3. If $f(x) \equiv x^3 + 3x$, simplify $f(x+\Delta x) - f(x)$.
4. If $f(x) \equiv \dfrac{1}{x}$, simplify $f(x+\Delta x) - f(x)$.

The notation $\dfrac{dy}{dx}$

4·4. In § 2·9 we saw that $\dfrac{k}{h}$ measured the average gradient of the curve $y = x^2$ over the interval x to $x+h$. With the Δ notation, we should say $\dfrac{\Delta y}{\Delta x}$ measured the average gradient over the interval x to $x+\Delta x$.

The limit of $\dfrac{\Delta y}{\Delta x}$ as $\Delta x \to 0$ is the gradient of the graph at the point given by x; it is what we have hitherto called $\mathsf{D}_x y$. But the more

* Δ is a Greek capital D; δ, the small Greek d, is often used in the same sense.

usual notation for this limit is $\frac{dy}{dx}$; thus the limit of $\frac{\Delta y}{\Delta x}$ as $\Delta x \to 0$ is $\frac{dy}{dx}$.

The reader should note carefully that $\frac{dy}{dx}$ is not a ratio or a quotient or a fraction; it is the limit which a certain fraction approaches; to remind us of this it is convenient to write it in a form that looks like a fraction.

The symbols, dy, dx written separately have no meaning at present. For instance, the limit of Δx is not dx, the limit of Δy is not dy. The symbol $\frac{dy}{dx}$ means neither more nor less than $\mathsf{D}_x y$, the derived function of y with respect to x.

The derived function of x^2 with respect to x may be written $\frac{d(x^2)}{dx}$; or more usually $\frac{d}{dx}(x^2)$. The derived function of $2x^2 - x$ with respect to x is written $\frac{d}{dx}(2x^2 - x)$; and so forth.

4·5. To differentiate x^3. Let $y = x^3$; and suppose that when x is increased to $x + \Delta x$, y is increased to $y + \Delta y$.

Then
$$y + \Delta y = (x + \Delta x)^3$$
$$= x^3 + 3x^2\Delta x + 3x(\Delta x)^2 + (\Delta x)^3.*$$
$$\therefore \Delta y = 3x^2\Delta x + 3x(\Delta x)^2 + (\Delta x)^3.$$
$$\therefore \frac{\Delta y}{\Delta x} = 3x^2 + 3x\Delta x + (\Delta x)^2, \quad \text{if} \quad \Delta x \neq 0.$$

Therefore, as $\Delta x \to 0$, $\frac{\Delta y}{\Delta x} \to 3x^2$.

$$\therefore \frac{dy}{dx} = 3x^2, \quad \text{or} \quad \frac{d}{dx}(x^3) = 3x^2.$$

4·6. To differentiate $\frac{1}{x}$. Let $y = \frac{1}{x}$; and suppose that when x is increased to $x + \Delta x$, y is increased to $y + \Delta y$.

* Note that the bracket is essential in $(\Delta x)^2$, $(\Delta x)^3$. Why?

Then
$$y+\Delta y = \frac{1}{x+\Delta x}.$$

$$\therefore\ \Delta y = \frac{1}{x+\Delta x} - \frac{1}{x}$$
$$= \frac{x-(x+\Delta x)}{x(x+\Delta x)}$$
$$= \frac{-\Delta x}{x(x+\Delta x)}.$$

$$\therefore\ \frac{\Delta y}{\Delta x} = -\frac{1}{x^2+x\Delta x},\quad \text{if}\quad \Delta x \neq 0.$$

Now, as $\Delta x \to 0$, $\dfrac{\Delta y}{\Delta x} \to -\dfrac{1}{x^2}$.

$$\therefore\ \frac{dy}{dx} = -\frac{1}{x^2},\quad \text{or}\quad \frac{d}{dx}\left(\frac{1}{x}\right) = -\frac{1}{x^2}.$$

4·7. Recapitulation of results. We have now differentiated the following powers of x; namely x^3, x^2, x, $\dfrac{1}{x}$. We may regard 1 as a power of x, since $x^0 = 1$. Also $\dfrac{1}{x} = x^{-1}$ and $\dfrac{1}{x^2} = x^{-2}$. The results obtained are

If $y =$	x^3	x^2	x^1	x^0	x^{-1}
$\dfrac{dy}{dx} =$	$3x^2$	$2x$	$1 . x^0$	0	$-1 . x^{-2}$

In Chapter 7 the method is shown of differentiating *any* power of x. Can you, by examining the above table, suggest any general law for the derived function of x^n? The general law is a help to memorizing the above results.

Exercise 4*c*

Nos. 1–6 *are intended for class discussion*

1. Show that the gradient of $y = x^3$ is always positive. What does this mean?

2. The point (2, 8) is on $y = x^3$. What is the gradient at this point?

3. What is the gradient of $y = x^3$ (i) where $x = -\frac{1}{2}$, (ii) where $y = -27$?

4. Where does $y=x^3$ slope at 45° ?

5. Show that the gradient of $y=\frac{1}{x}$ is always negative. What does this mean?

6. At what point does the curve $y=\frac{1}{x}$ slope at an angle of 45° or 135°?

---

7. What is the gradient of the curve $y = x^3+3x^2-9x+1$ at the point where $x=1$? Interpret this graphically by means of a rough sketch.

Is there any other point on the curve with the same gradient?

8. Find the gradient of the tangent to the curve $y = x^2(x+3)$ at the point where it cuts the axis of x.

9. Find the gradient of the tangent to the curve

$$y = 2x^3-15x^2+36x-21$$

at the point (1, 2).

At what other point of the curve is the tangent parallel to the tangent at the point (1, 2)?

10. Find the slopes of $y=\frac{1}{x}$ and $y=x^3$ at the points where the two curves cut. Mark on a sketch the points and the tangents at these points.

11. Show by means of the value of $\frac{dy}{dx}$ that, in the curve

$$y = 2x^3-3x^2+4,$$

as x increases from 0 onwards the value of y at first decreases, but subsequently begins to increase and continues to do so. Show also that the slope of the curve may have any positive value, but that certain negative values, for instance -2, are not possible.

---

12. Prove that the graphs $y = 2x^2-x$ and $y = \frac{3}{x}+14$ have a common point when $x=3$. Find the gradient of each graph at this point.

13. If P is a point on the curve $y=x^3$ and the tangent at P meets Ox in Q and Oy in R, express OQ in terms of the x co-ordinate of P and show that PR = 3PQ.

14. If $y=\frac{100}{x}$ what is $\frac{dy}{dx}$? Show that if the tangent at P to this curve meets the axes at A and B respectively, the triangle AOB contains 200 units of area.

Check the result by taking a simple special case.

15. The curve whose equation is

$$y = ax^3 + bx^2 + cx$$

(a, b and c constants) has a slope of 45° at the origin and touches Ox at the point $(1, 0)$.

Find from these data the values of a, b, c.

Maxima and minima

4·8. Fig. 4·1 shows the graph $y = 16x(x-1)(x^2-1)+5$.

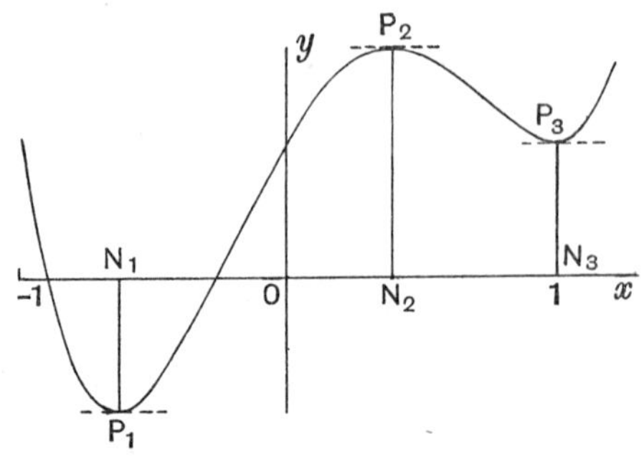

Fig. 4·1

At P_1, P_2, P_3 the gradient of the curve is zero; at P_2 the y of the curve is said to have a maximum value, at P_1 and P_3 the y of the curve has minimum values. In other words

$$y \text{ [i.e. } 16x(x-1)(x^2-1)+5]$$

has a minimum value when x = about $-\frac{5}{8}$, a maximum value when x = about $\frac{3}{8}$ and another minimum value when $x = 1$.

Notice that, though N_2P_2 is a maximum value for y, it is not the greatest value that y can have. In fact maximum and minimum values are not the same as greatest and least values; a **maximum value** is a value that is greater than the values on either side of it; in the same way a **minimum value** is a value that is smaller than the values on either side of it.

Just to the left of P_2 the gradient is positive; just to the right it is negative; at P_2 the gradient is zero. We see that as P passes through a maximum towards the right, the gradient changes from + to − through zero.

How does the gradient change in passing through a minimum?

Points at which a function has a maximum or a minimum value are classed together as **turning points**, and the maximum and minimum values are called **turning values**. At every such point the function, after increasing, 'turns' and begins to decrease; or vice versa.

To search for turning points of a function it is necessary to find values of x at which the gradient of the graph is zero, or the derived function of the function is zero.

4·9. Note on the terms 'greater' and 'less' as applied to negative numbers. -3 is said to be *greater* than -12. *Numerically*, -3 is less than -12; but from an algebraical point of view it is greater. The terms 'greater' and 'less' are always presumed to bear the algebraical meaning, unless the contrary is stated, i.e. unless we say 'numerically greater' or 'numerically less'.

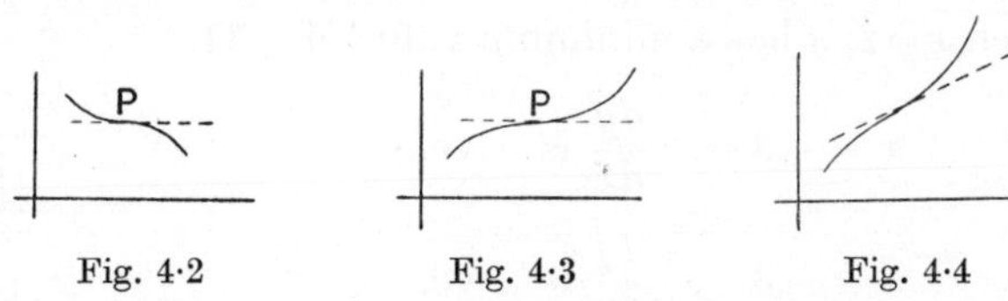

Fig. 4·2 Fig. 4·3 Fig. 4·4

Before we can establish that a certain value of x, say $x=a$, gives a maximum or a minimum value of $f(x)$, we must make sure that the gradient changes sign as we pass from one side of $x=a$ to the other. The necessity for this is made clear by figs. 4·2 and 4·3. In each case, the gradient at P is zero, but neither shows a maximum or a minimum. In fig. 4·2 what is the sign of the gradient to the left of P? what to the right? In fig. 4·3 what is the sign of the gradient to the left and to the right of P?

The curves in figs. 4·2 and 4·3 are said to have a **point of inflexion** at P. It is not, however, necessary that the tangent should be parallel to the x axis at a point of inflexion; thus fig. 4·4 shows a point of inflexion.

Example 2. Find the maximum and minimum values of $2x^3+3x^2-36x+10$.

Let y denote the given function of x.

Then $$\frac{dy}{dx} = 6x^2+6x-36 = 6(x-2)(x+3).$$

y has maximum or minimum values where $\frac{dy}{dx}=0$, i.e. where $x=2$ or -3.

When $x = 2$, $\quad y = 16+12-72+10 = -34.$

When $x = -3$, $\quad y = -54+27+108+10 = 91.$

To find whether these values are maxima or minima, we must examine the sign of $\frac{dy}{dx}$ near these points.

If $\quad x = 2+, \quad \frac{dy}{dx}$ is $+$ve.

If $\quad x = 2-, \quad \frac{dy}{dx}$ is $-$ve.

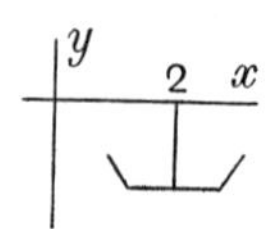

Fig. 4·5

$\therefore$ when $x=2$, y has a minimum value of -34.

If $\quad x = -3+, \quad \frac{dy}{dx}$ is $-$ve.

If $\quad x = -3-, \quad \frac{dy}{dx}$ is $+$ve.

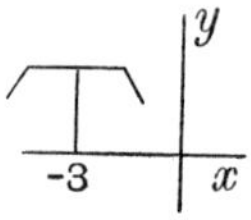

Fig. 4·6

$\therefore$ when $x = -3$, y has a maximum value of 91.

Exercise 4*d*

1. Write down the value of $\frac{d}{dx}\left(\frac{1}{3}x^3 - 2x^2 - \frac{3}{x}\right)$.

2. Write down the derived functions of

(i) $10-\frac{2}{3}x^3+\frac{1}{2x}-\frac{1}{2}x^2$, (ii) $-\frac{3}{5x}+\frac{1}{6}x^3-7$,

(iii) $3x-5+4x^3-6x^2-\frac{3}{x}$, (iv) $3x^2-4x+\frac{7}{x}$.

3. Differentiate the following (first remove brackets):

(i) $2x(3+x^2)$, (ii) $\frac{1}{x}(3+4x+5x^2+6x^3)$,

(iii) $x(2+3x)^2$, (iv) $\frac{4x^5-3x}{x^2}-\frac{2x^3-4x}{x}$.

4. Find the gradient of the curve $xy = a^2$ at the point where $x = 2a$.

5. If $R = 2\theta(a - b\theta^2)$, find $\frac{dR}{d\theta}$ where a, b are constant.

¶6. For what values of x are the following expressions positive? for what values are they negative?

(i) $(x-5)(x-1)$, (ii) $(x-1)(x-2)(x-3)$,
(iii) $(2-x)(x-4)$, (iv) $(3+x)(5-x)$,
(v) $(x-1)^2(3-x)$, (vi) $(x^2-1)(x^2-4)$.

7. Show that the expression $x^3 - 9x^2 + 24x - 7$ decreases in value as x increases from 2 to 4, and after that increases as x increases.

8. Investigate the maxima and minima of the following functions:

(i) $x^3 - 3x$, (ii) $\frac{x^3}{3} - 2x^2 + 3x$, (iii) $4x + \frac{1}{x}$,

(iv) $(x-2)(x+1)^2$, (v) $\frac{x^2}{2} + \frac{1}{x}$, (vi) $\frac{3(x^2 + \frac{1}{2})}{4x}$.

9. Find $\frac{dy}{dx}$, where $y = 24x + 3x^2 - x^3$.

Prove that y has a maximum value 80 where $x = 4$.
When $x = -5$, y has again the value 80. Explain this.

10. When is the sum of a number and its reciprocal a minimum? a maximum?

11. Find the differential coefficient of $x + \frac{4}{x}$, and show that this expression cannot have any value intermediate between 4 and -4.

---

12. Investigate the maxima and minima of the following functions:

(i) $6x^2 - 9x - x^3 - 1$, (ii) $(x-1)(x-2)^2$, (iii) $x(x-2)^2 + 5$,

(iv) $x(x^2-9)$, (v) $x(x-5)(x-8)$, (vi) $\frac{x^3}{3} - 5x - \frac{4}{x}$.

13. Find the value of x for which the sum of the corresponding ordinates of the curves

$$y = 2x^3 - 15x^2 + 36x + 5 \quad \text{and} \quad y = x^2 - 4x + 3$$

is a maximum, and show that, for this value, the corresponding ordinate of one curve is a maximum while that of the other is a minimum.

14. Write down the gradient of the function $4x^2 + \frac{27}{x}$. Hence find the value of x for which the function is a maximum or a minimum. Which is it?

¶ For discussion.

Exercise 4e

Mainly solid geometry

1. The area of a rectangle is 100 sq.in. and one of its sides is x in. What is its perimeter? When is the perimeter least?

2. A rectangular solid has a square base. Its combined length, breadth and depth add up to 14 ft. If the length and breadth are each x ft., what is the depth? Write down in terms of x an expression for the volume. Find the value of x for which this volume is greatest. What is this maximum volume?

3. A rectangular sheet of metal is 8 by 3 in. Four equal squares, side x in., are removed one from each corner. The edges left are then turned up to be perpendicular to the base, and so form a box. Show that it holds $(4x^3-22x^2+24x)$ cu.in.

Find the value of x that makes this volume greatest.

---

4. From a rectangular sheet of cardboard ABCD (see fig. 4·7) the shaded pieces are cut out at the corners; the remainder is folded so as to form a rectangular box with a lid. If $AB=a$, $BC=b$, and x is the length of a side of each of the squares cut out at the two bottom corners, find an expression for the volume of the box.

If $a=6$ in., $b=12$ in., find approximately the value of x for which the volume is a maximum. What is the maximum volume?

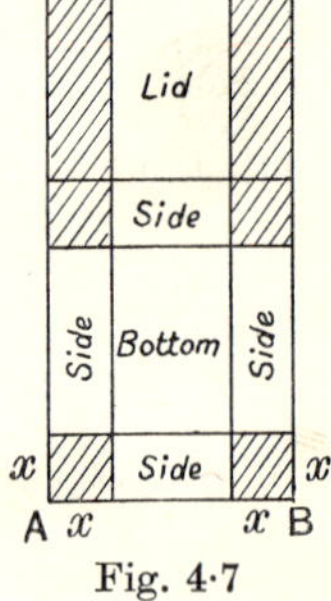

Fig. 4·7

5. A manufacturer makes open boxes of thin sheet iron standing on a square base and each containing 40 cu.in. Show that when a side of the base is x in. the area of the sheet iron used is $\left(\frac{160}{x}+x^2\right)$ sq.in.

Find the dimensions of the box when the area of sheet iron used is least.

6. An open vessel of thin material has a square horizontal base and four vertical rectangular sides. Show that, if the volume V is kept constant, and a, the length of the edge of the base, varies, the total surface is least when $a^3=2V$.

---

7. A cylindrical gasometer whose one closed end is flat is to have a capacity of ten million cubic feet. If the radius is x ft. and the area of sheet metal y sq.ft., prove that $y=\pi x^2+\frac{2\times 10^7}{x}$.

Find the least value of y.

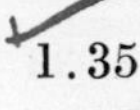

8. A cylindrical vessel is to be made out of 100 sq.in. of sheet tin. It has no lid. If the radius of the base is x in., show that the volume is

$$\left(50x - \frac{\pi}{2}x^3\right) \text{cu.in.}$$

What is the greatest volume of the vessel?

9. An open cylindrical vessel is to be constructed from a given amount of uniform thin material. Show that it contains the greatest possible volume when its height is equal to the radius of its base.

10. Find the height of the right circular cone of maximum volume, the sum of the height and radius of the base being 12 in.

11. A cylinder is inscribed in a given sphere, find when the cylinder has maximum volume. (Let the height of the cylinder be $2x$ units.)

---

12. A cone of height h is inscribed in a sphere of radius R. Find an expression for its volume.

Write down the gradient of this expression regarded as a function of h and show that the greatest volume of a cone inscribed in the sphere is the volume of a sphere of radius $\frac{2}{3}$R.

13. A match-box, made of wood of negligible thickness, is c in. long and consists of a box, open at the top, and a cover, open at both ends, into which the box slides. Take x in. as the breadth and y in. as the depth of the box and cover and suppose that the volume of the box is given equal to a^2c cu.in. Express the area of wood required for the box and cover in terms of x, a, c; find the ratio of x to y so that this may be a minimum, when a and c are given.

14. The Parcel Post regulations require that the sum of the length and girth of a parcel shall not exceed 6 ft. Girth means measurement round. If it is desired to send the greatest possible volume, find the length of the parcel (i) if it is a prism with square section (let side of section $= x$ ft.), (ii) if it is a cylinder. Also find the volume in each case.

Exercise 4*f*

1. Sketch on squared paper from $x=0$ to $x = 1$, the curve

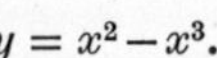

$$y = x^2 - x^3.$$

The figure obtained describes the section of a hill if unit x represents 1 mile and unit y represents 400 ft.

By calculation find

(i) the height of the hill;

(ii) the height of the point between the two positions of zero gradient at which the slope of the hill-side is greatest, and also the gradient there.

2. An open rectangular tank whose depth is y ft. and base a square of side x ft. (inside measurements) is to have an inside capacity a^3 cu.ft. It is made of two pieces of metal riveted at the four sides of the base, and along one of the vertical sides. If the cost of riveting is £b per foot length of riveted seam measured inside, find the proportions of the tank for which the cost of the riveting will be a minimum. Give a common-sense reason as to why this cost is a minimum and not a maximum.

3. The strength of a rectangular beam of given length varies as xy^2, where x in. is the breadth and y in. the depth. Find the depth and breadth of the strongest rectangular beam of perimeter 3 ft.

4. Under certain conditions, the strength of a rectangular beam of given length varies as the product of the breadth and the square of the depth. Given a cylindrical tree trunk of diameter d in., what is the ratio of depth to breadth for the strongest rectangular beam that can be cut from it? (Take x in. as the breadth of the beam.)

5. When a certain ship is steaming at v knots the coal consumption per hour is known to be $(0{\cdot}25+0{\cdot}002v^3)$ ton. The constant expenses per hour for wages, upkeep, etc., work out at the cost of 1·5 tons of coal. Find the cost of steaming 1000 sea-miles at v knots, assuming the coal to cost £c per ton. Now determine v so that this cost may be least.

---

6. On a certain steamer the cost of coal per mile is found to be directly proportional to the square of the speed maintained, being 2*s*. 6*d*. per mile when the speed is 30 miles per hour; the other expenses being £1. 16*s*. per hour at all speeds. Express in pounds the expense of a journey of 100 miles at x miles an hour. Hence find the most economical speed and the expense at that speed.

7. In running an express train from London to Edinburgh the cost is £$\left(a\mathsf{V}+\frac{b}{\mathsf{V}}\right)$, where V miles per hour is the average velocity of the train, and a, b are constants. When the train travels at the rate of 30 miles an hour the cost is £75; when it runs at 40 miles an hour the cost is £65. Find the values of a and b. Hence find the most economical speed and the expense at that speed.

8. It is found that the cost of running a certain steamer a certain definite distance, at an average speed of V knots, is proportional to $\mathsf{V}+\frac{\mathsf{V}^3}{100}+\frac{300}{\mathsf{V}}$, the first two terms representing the cost of power and the third term the costs, such as wages, which are directly proportional to the time occupied. What is the most economical speed?

9. Soreau's formulae for the supporting thrust V and the horizontal thrust H of the air on a plane surface making a small angle α with the direction of motion are

$$H = kv^2(a\alpha^2+b),$$
$$V = kv^2\alpha,$$

where v is the velocity of the plane and k, a, b are constants. For what value of α is the ratio $\frac{H}{V}$ a minimum?

Exercise 4*g*

Velocity and Acceleration

1. A particle moves in a straight line in such a way that its distance from a fixed point O in the line at the end of t sec. is

$$(17+5t+3t^3) \text{ ft.}$$

Find (i) its distance from O, (ii) its speed, (iii) its acceleration, at the end of 4 sec.

2. Repeat No. 1 for $s = 5-3t+7t^2-t^3$.

3. The distance (s ft.) passed over by a body in t sec. is given by

$$s = 4t-5t^2+2t^3.$$

Find the velocity and acceleration after 3 sec.

4. A point moves along a straight line so that, at the end of t sec., its distance (s ft.) from a fixed point on the line is given by the equation

$$s = t^3+2t^2+3t+4;$$

find the velocity and the acceleration at the end of 3 sec. and 4 sec., and the distance passed over in the fourth second.

5. A point moves in a straight line so that its distance (s ft.) from a fixed origin O at time t sec. is given by

$$s = 10+8t-3t^2+\tfrac{1}{3}t^3.$$

(i) Find the position of the point at zero time.
(ii) Find the velocity at time t.
(iii) At what instants does the velocity vanish?
(iv) What is the acceleration at these instants?

6. A point is moving in a straight line so that its distance from a fixed point O of that line is $(27t-t^3)$ in. at t sec. Prove that it will move outwards from O for 3 sec., and that when it returns to O its speed will be 54 in. per sec.

---

7. If $s = t^3+7t$ (s being measured in feet and t in seconds), find

(i) average speed between $t=2$ and $t=3$,
(ii) arithmetic mean of the speeds at the instants $t=2$ and $t=3$,
(iii) speed at the instant $t=2\tfrac{1}{2}$.

8. If a body be moving in a straight line and its distance (s ft.) from a fixed point in the line after t sec. is given by $s = 5+2t+t^3$, find

(i) the average speed during the 5th second,
(ii) the speed at the end of $4\frac{1}{2}$ sec.,
(iii) the acceleration at the end of $4\frac{1}{2}$ sec.

9. If $s = a+bt+ct^2+dt^3$ with usual notation, and a, b, c, d are constants, find

(i) average velocity between the end of 2nd and 4th second,
(ii) velocity at the end of 3 sec.,
(iii) acceleration at the end of 3 sec.

10. A body moves in a straight line in such a way that its distance (s ft.) from a fixed point O in the line at the end of t sec. is given by $s = 11+2t^3$. Find its distances from O at the end of 4, $4+h$, $4-h$ sec. Hence find the average speeds

(i) during the interval of h sec. immediately following the end of the 4th second;
(ii) during the interval of h sec. immediately preceding the end of the 4th second;
(iii) during the interval of $2h$ sec., which is the sum of these two intervals.

Show that by making h small enough, each of these average speeds can be brought as near as we like to 96 ft. per sec. What is this speed of 96 ft. per sec. called?

Exercise 4*h*

Small increases and rates of change

1. A cube, length of side x, has volume V. Find $\frac{dV}{dx}$.

A cube of side 12 in. is heated uniformly so that each side becomes 12·3 in. Use the above result to find approximately the increase in volume. What is the exact value of the increase in volume?

2. The volume of a cube is increasing at the rate of 3 cu.in. per sec. Find at what rate the length of a side and the area of a face are increasing when the length of a side is 6 in.

3. If the radius of a sphere is increased from 10 to 10·1 cm., find approximately by how much its volume has increased?

4. The radius of a sphere is increasing at the rate of 0·02 in. per min.; at a certain instant the radius is 10 in.; find at what rate the volume of the sphere is increasing at that instant.

5. The volume of a sphere is increasing uniformly at the rate of 1 cu.in. per sec. Find at what rate the radius is growing (i) when the radius is 3 in., (ii) when the radius is 10 in.

Find also at what rates the surface area is growing for the same values of the radius.

6. A vessel containing water is in the form of an inverted hollow pyramid; its base is a square of side 6 ft., and altitude of pyramid is 10 ft. If depth be x ft., what is the volume of water?

If water flows in at the rate of 10 cu.ft. per min., at what rate is the level of water rising when the depth is 4 ft.?

---

7. A hemispherical bowl of radius 1 ft. is partly filled with water. If the depth of water is x in., and y sq.in. the area of the water-surface, express y in terms of x.

If water is poured in at such a rate that x increases uniformly at $\frac{1}{2}$ in. per sec., find a formula for the time-rate at which y increases, and give the numerical result when $x=6$.

8. A vessel containing water is in the form of an inverted hollow cone with vertical angle 90°. If the depth of water be x ft., what is the volume of water?

If water flows in at the rate of 2 cu.ft. per min., at what rate is the level of water rising when the depth is 2 ft.?

9. The volume of a spherical cap of height h cut off from a sphere of radius r is $\pi h^2(r-\frac{1}{3}h)$. Use this result to solve the following problem:

A hemispherical bowl has a diameter of 4 ft. Water is pouring into it from a tap at the rate of 33 cu.in. per sec. At what rate (inches per second) is the depth of the water in the bottom of the bowl rising at the instant when this depth is 6 in.?

10. A solid is formed by placing a hemisphere of radius x in. on one end of a cylinder of radius x in. and of height 12 in. Express the volume (V) as a function of x.

If R_1 and R_2 are the rates of increase of V with x when $x=9$ in. and when $x=10\frac{1}{2}$ in. show that

$$5R_1 = 4R_2.$$

11. A spherical soap bubble is of radius r and volume v. If r is subject to slight variation, show that the percentage increase (supposed small) in r is one-third of the percentage increase in v.

If r increases from 1 in. to 1·05 in. find, approximately, the increase in v.

12. At a given instant the radii of two concentric spheres are 8 ft. and 2 ft.; the radius of the outer sphere is increasing at the rate of 2 in. per sec., and the radius of the inner one is increasing at the rate of 3 in. per sec. Find the rate at which the volume between the spheres is changing.

13. If the volume of a cone remains constant while the radius of its base is increasing at the rate of 1 % per sec., find the percentage rate per second at which its height is diminishing.

CHAPTER 5

INTEGRATION AS ANTI-DIFFERENTIATION

5·1. If $y=x^3$, then $\frac{dy}{dx}=3x^2$. The latter statement is called a **differential equation,** i.e. an equation involving one or more derived functions.

If we are told that $\frac{dy}{dx}=3x^2$, what information have we about y? Clearly we are *not* told directly that y is a certain function of x. We are told that the derived function of y is a certain function of x. Can we from this find y as a function of x?

In differentiation, we solve the problem: given a function, find the derived function.

The inverse problem—given the derived function, find the original function—is the problem of **anti-differentiation** or **integration.**

To solve the differential equation

$$\frac{dy}{dx}=3x^2$$

we have to solve a problem of integration.

Now it is clear that one solution of this differential equation is

$$y=x^3.$$

But is this the only solution possible? What is the value of $\frac{d}{dx}(x^3+1)$? of $\frac{d}{dx}(x^3+2)$? Can you suggest a more general solution than x^3?

It will be seen that $y = x^3+c$, where c is a constant, satisfies the differential equation $\frac{dy}{dx}=3x^2$. This statement is to be verified by differentiating x^3+c. As regards the constant c, any value will do; c is called an **arbitrary** constant.

5·2. Given the fact that $\frac{dy}{dx}=3x^2$, we are given the gradient of a graph for every value of x; the problem of integration is the problem of deducing the graph. Why do we get a solution involving an arbitrary constant? If we compare the various curves obtained by giving different values to c, e.g. $y=x^3$, $y=x^3+1$, $y=x^3+2$, $y=x^3-1$, etc., we see that they are really the same curve, moved higher up or lower down on the paper. Thus $y=x^3+1$ differs from $y=x^3$ simply in this, that the whole curve lies 1 unit higher. Now this shifting of the whole curve up or down does not alter the gradient for any value of x; it alters y, but does not alter $\frac{dy}{dx}$. This explains why every graph obtained by giving different values to c in $y=x^3+c$ should satisfy the same condition as regards gradient.

Thus we say that, if $\frac{dy}{dx}=3x^2$, then $y=x^3+c$, or x^3+c is the result of anti-differentiating or integrating $3x^2$ with respect to x, or the **integral** of $3x^2$ is x^3+c.

Exercise 5*a*

Suitable for oral work

Solve the following differential equations:

1. $\frac{dy}{dx}=2x.$ 2. $\frac{dy}{dx}=x.$ 3. $\frac{dy}{dx}=ax.$

4. $\frac{dy}{dx}=x^2.$ 5. $\frac{dy}{dx}=ax^2.$ 6. $\frac{dy}{dx}=px^2+qx+r.$

7. $\frac{dy}{dx}=-\frac{1}{x^2}.$ 8. $\frac{dy}{dt}=\frac{2}{t^2}.$ 9. $\frac{dy}{dt}=\frac{a}{t^2}+b+ct.$

5·3. Note that x^2 is obtained by differentiating x^3,

x is obtained by differentiating x^2,

a constant is obtained by differentiating x,

$\frac{1}{x^2}$ or x^{-2} is obtained by differentiating $\frac{1}{x}$ or x^{-1}.

If you have to anti-differentiate, or integrate, an expression such as $5x^2-7x+3+\frac{4}{x^2}$, it is best for the $5x^2$ term to write $5x^3$, then differentiate, giving $5 \times 3x^2$, and consider what adjustment you must make in the coefficient of x^3 so that the result is $5x^2$—clearly the term should be $\frac{5}{3}x^3$. Then for the term $-7x$ write $-7x^2$, differentiate and adjust. Similarly for each term.

Exercise 5*b*

1. What is the result of anti-differentiating, or integrating, with respect to x, the following:

(i) $4x^2 - 5x + 1$, (ii) $2x - 1 - \dfrac{5}{x^2}$, (iii) $7x^2 + 4 + \dfrac{2}{x^2}$,

(iv) $\frac{1}{3}x^2 + \frac{1}{2}x - \dfrac{1}{3x^2}$, (v) $(x-1)(x-2)$, (vi) $x^2\left(2 - \dfrac{3}{x^2} + \dfrac{4}{x^4}\right)$,

(vii) $\dfrac{(x+1)(x-1)}{x^2}$, (viii) $\dfrac{(x^2+3)(x^2-4)}{x^2}$, (ix) $\dfrac{x^5 - 3x^3 + 4x}{x^3}$.

2. Find the equation of the curve which passes through the point (2, 5) and is such that, at the point (x, y),

$$\frac{dy}{dx} = 3x^2 - 8x + 4.$$

3. A curve passes through the origin, and its gradient function is $2x - \frac{1}{2}x^2$; find its ordinate at $x = 2$.

4. The gradient of a curve at the point (x, y) is $1 - \dfrac{4}{x^2}$. Find the equation of the curve if it passes through the point (1, 1).

5. A curve passes through the point (0, 2), and, at any point (x, y) of this curve, $\dfrac{dy}{dx} = 3x^2 - 4x - 1$. Find where the curve cuts the axis of x.

The integral notation

5·4.* In § 5·1 we have seen that, if $\dfrac{dy}{dx} = 3x^2$, then $y = x^3 + c$. This fact may be stated thus $\int 3x^2\,dx = x^3 + c$. This is called the integral notation. Its significance is explained on pp. 1.88 to 1.90.

* This article may be omitted.

Exercise 5*c*

Find the following integrals:

1. $\int 2x\,dx.$ 2. $\int x^2\,dx.$ 3. $\int 3\,dx.$

4. $\int \frac{1}{x^2}\,dx.$ 5. $\int ax\,dx.$ 6. $\int \frac{5}{t^2}\,dt.$

7. $\int (pt^2+qt+r)\,dt.$ 8. $\int \left(5t^2-\frac{6}{t^2}\right)dt.$

9. $\int (x-2)(x+3)\,dx.$ 10. $\int \frac{(x+2)(x-2)}{x^2}\,dx.$

11. $\int t^2\left(3-\frac{5}{t^2}+\frac{1}{t^4}\right)dt.$ 12. $\int \frac{(x^2-5)(x^2+2)}{x^2}\,dx.$

Work Exercise 5*b*, No. 1, using the integral notation.

5·5. Given time-velocity law, to find time-space law. In the case of a point moving in a straight line, if we know the law connecting distance with time, we can find the velocity, and hence the acceleration, by a process of differentiation.

In the inverse problem, we may be given the law connecting velocity and time, and required to find the distance. If the law is the simplest possible, i.e. that of uniform velocity, we can use arithmetic to find the distance. But suppose that the velocity is known to vary as the time; i.e. $v=kt$; or in other words

$$\frac{ds}{dt} = kt.$$

The solution of this differential equation is

$$s = \tfrac{1}{2}kt^2+c \quad \text{(verify by differentiating).}$$

We cannot find the value of c unless we have some further information; e.g. the position of the point at some instant of time. Suppose that the point is at the 2 ft. mark when $t=0$.

Then $$2 = 0+c; \quad \therefore\ c = 2,$$

$$\therefore\ s=\tfrac{1}{2}kt^2+2.$$

Exercise 5*d*

Find the law connecting time and distance when the time-velocity law is given as follows, Nos. 1–3.

1. $v = 2+3t$; and $s=3$ when $t=0$.

2. $v = t^2+4t-5$; and $s=4$ when $t=1$.

3. $v = 2-\dfrac{1}{t^2}$; and $s=3$ when $t=1$.

4. A body moves in a straight line so that its velocity, v ft. per sec., t sec. after passing a point O is given by $v = 10-8t$. Find the position of the body after 3 sec. and the distance it travels between the ends of the 5th and 10th seconds. Explain the negative answers.

Find the law connecting time and distance when the time-velocity law is given as follows, Nos. 5–7:

5. $v = t^2+\dfrac{1}{t^2}$; and $s=4$ when $t=2$.

6. $v = (t-1)(t-3)$; and $s=5$ when $t=0$.

7. $v = \dfrac{t^2-1}{t^2}$; and $s=6$ when $t=1$.

8. A point moves along a straight line so that, at the end of t sec., its velocity (v ft. per sec.) is given by the equation $v = 3t^2+4t+3$. Find the acceleration of the point at the moment when $t=3$ and the distance the point covers during the fourth second.

9. A stopping train runs between two consecutive stations with a velocity given by the law $\frac{1}{2}t(2-t)$, velocity being measured in miles per minute and time being reckoned in minutes. Find
   (i) the time taken between the two stations;
   (ii) the maximum velocity attained;
   (iii) the distance between the two stations.

10. Repeat No. 9 for the law $v = \frac{1}{4}(t-1)(4-t)$.

5·6. Given time-acceleration law, to find time-velocity and time-space laws. Suppose that the acceleration (a units) of a point moving in a straight line is known to follow the law $b+ct$.

Then $$a = \frac{dv}{dt} = b+ct.$$

$$\therefore\ v = bt+\tfrac{1}{2}ct^2+k.$$

To find k we must have another datum. Suppose that $v=3$ when $t=0$; then

$$3 = 0+0+k,$$

$$\therefore\ v = bt+\tfrac{1}{2}ct^2+3,$$

and the time-velocity law is now known.

From this we may find the time-space law.

Exercise 5*e*

1. A stone is thrown vertically downwards with a velocity of 100 ft. per sec., and the downward acceleration due to gravity is 32 ft. per sec. per sec. Find the velocity t sec. later, and also the distance covered.

2. A stone is thrown vertically upwards with a velocity of 100 ft. per sec., and the downward acceleration due to gravity is 32 ft. per sec. per sec. Find the velocity t sec. later, and also the distance covered.

3. A body moves in a straight line in such a way that its acceleration t sec. after it has passed a fixed point O on the line is $3t$ ft. per sec. per sec. Find its distance from O after 5 sec., given that its speed when it passes O is 10 ft. per sec.

4. A body moves in a straight line under an acceleration governed by the law $a = 2+6t$, the units of space and time being feet and seconds respectively. When $t=0$, $s=4$ and $v=-2$. How far does the body move during the 3rd second? Show that the velocity is a minimum when the acceleration is zero, and that this velocity is $2\frac{1}{3}$ ft. per sec. in the negative direction.

5. A body moves in a straight line, and the acceleration is given as the following function of the time: $3t^2+t-2$; and $v=10$ when $t=1$; investigate the minimum and maximum values of the velocity.

Also show that the body is instantaneously at rest at some time between $t=-2$ and $t=-3$.

---

6. A point moves along a straight line so that, at the end of t sec., its acceleration (a ft. per sec. per sec.) is given by the equation $a = t+2$. If the point started from rest, find its velocity at the end of 3 sec., and the distance covered during the next second.

7. A point moves in a straight line from rest so that its acceleration is $15-3t$, where t is the number of seconds from the start. Prove that it next comes to rest again in 10 sec.

Find the distance moved during this time.

8. A point moves on a straight line so that its acceleration (a ft. per sec. per sec.) at the end of t sec. is given by the equation $a = 2t+3$. Find the

distance traversed during the fifth second of the motion if the point starts from rest.

9. A point is moving along a straight line with acceleration $(2+3t)$ ft./sec.^{2} at time t sec. At zero time its distance from the origin is 5 ft.; and at time $t=1$ its velocity is 10 ft./sec. Where is it at time $t=1$?

Area under a graph

5·7. The following example shows how integration may be used to find an area.

Example 1. Find the area bounded by the curve $y = 5+\frac{1}{10}x^2$, the x-axis, and the ordinates $x=2$ and $x=10$.

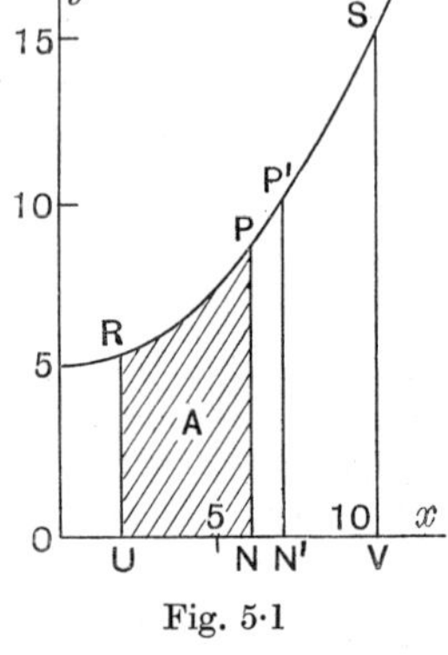

Fig. 5·1

In fig. 5·1, we want to find the area URSV.

Let P be any point (x, y) on the curve; draw PN the ordinate of P.

Let A represent the area URPN.

Now let PN move to a near position P′N′ and let Δx, Δy, ΔA be the corresponding increments of x, y, A.

Then ΔA is the area NPP′N′.

[Now the area NPP′N′ lies between the area of a rectangle of width NN′ and height NP and that of a rectangle of width NN′ and height N′P′.]

$$\therefore \ \Delta A \text{ lies between } y\Delta x \text{ and } (y+\Delta y)\,\Delta x.$$

$$\therefore \ \frac{\Delta A}{\Delta x} \text{ lies between } y \text{ and } y+\Delta y.$$

Now as $\Delta x \to 0$, $\dfrac{\Delta A}{\Delta x} \to \dfrac{dA}{dx}$ and $\Delta y \to 0$.

$$\therefore \ \frac{dA}{dx} = y.$$

$$\therefore \ \frac{dA}{dx} = 5+\tfrac{1}{10}x^2.$$

$$\therefore \ A = 5x+\tfrac{1}{30}x^3+c.$$

When NP is brought back to UR, i.e. when $x = 2$, $A = 0$.

$$\therefore\ 0 = 5 \times 2 + \tfrac{1}{30} \times 2^3 + c. \qquad \text{(i)}$$

When NP is moved to VS, i.e. when $x = 10$, A is the required area.

$$\therefore\ \text{the required area} = 5 \times 10 + \tfrac{1}{30} \times 10^3 + c. \qquad \text{(ii)}$$

From (i) and (ii) by subtraction

$$\text{the required area} = 50 + \tfrac{100}{3} - 10 - \tfrac{8}{30} = 73\tfrac{1}{15}.$$

5·8. Note that the result $\dfrac{d}{dx}(\text{area}) = y$ is true whatever function y is of x. Later on we may assume this result, but for the present it will be wise to put the work out fully as above.

Exercise 5*f*

1. Find the area bounded by the parabola $y = 3 + 4x + 3x^2$, the axis of x, and (i) the ordinates at $x = 1$ and $x = 2$, (ii) the ordinates at $x = 1$ and $x = 5$.

2. Find the area enclosed between the curve $y = \dfrac{10}{x^2}$, the x-axis and the ordinates at $x = 2$, $x = 8$.

3. Find the area included between the curve whose equation is

$$x^2y = x^3 + a^3,$$

the axis of x, and the ordinates at $x = a$ and $x = 2a$.

---

4. The curve $y = x(2-x)(1+x)$ cuts the axis of x at the points A(2, 0), O(0, 0), B(−1, 0). Find the area included (i) between the curve and the line AO, (ii) between the curve and the line OB.

Do you get the same sign for these areas? If not, why not?

5. Find the area enclosed between the axis of x and the curve

$$y = 7x - x^2 - 10.$$

(At what points does the curve cut the x-axis?)

6. Find the area included between the axis of x and the portion of the curve $y = x^2 - 2x - 3$ which lies below that axis.

7. Find the area enclosed by the axis of x and that part of the curve $y = 5x - 6 - x^2$ for which y is positive.

---

8. Find the area of the part of the curve $y = x(2\tfrac{1}{2} - x)$ which lies above $y = 1$.

9. Find the area between the parabola $3y = x^2$ and the line $y = x + 6$.

10. Find the area which lies between the curve $y = 2x - 3x^3$ and the line $y = x$, and which is situated in the first quadrant.

11. Find the area bounded by the curve $y = x^2 - \frac{1}{x^2}$, the parabola $y = x^2$, and the ordinates at $x = a$, $x = b$.

---

12. Find the area enclosed between the lines $x = 0$, $x = 12$ and the curves $y = 2 + \frac{x}{20} - \frac{x^2}{200}$ and $y = \frac{x^2}{200} - 2 - \frac{x}{20}$.

13. P is a point on the parabola $y = x^2$; PN is drawn perpendicular to the x-axis; O is the origin. Prove that the area bounded by PN, ON, and the curve is $\frac{1}{3}$ of that of the rectangle whose sides are ON, PN.

14. Prove that the parabolas $y^2 = 4x$ and $x^2 = 4y$ divide into three equal parts the square bounded by the lines $x = 4$, $y = 4$, and the axes of co-ordinates.

15. Find the area included between the curve $y = x^2$, the axis Ox, and the ordinate $x = 10$. Where would you draw a line perpendicular to Ox to bisect this area?

16. Prove that the area of the curve $y = a + bx + cx^2$ between the ordinates at $x = -d$ and $x = +d$ and the axis of x is $2ad + \frac{2}{3}cd^3$.

Hence show that if h_1, h_2 and h_3 are the ordinates of this curve at the points $x = -d$, $x = 0$, and $x = +d$ respectively, the area in question is equal to $\frac{d}{3}(h_1 + 4h_2 + h_3)$.

---

17. In the curve whose equation is $y = 5x - x^2$, at what rate with respect to x is the area between the curve, the axis Ox, and an ordinate PM increasing as M moves along the axis Ox?

If M is moving at 3 ft. per sec. and all dimensions are in feet, give the rate of increase of area when $x = 1$.

18. Where does the curve $y = x - \frac{1}{x^2}$ cut the axis of x? Find the area below the curve from this point to $x = 2$.

If x is increasing at a rate v, at what rate is the area growing?

Volume of solid of revolution

5·9. If any line (straight or curved) be made to rotate about a straight line, it generates a surface called a **surface of revolution**. Thus, a straight line rotating about a parallel straight line generates a circular cylinder; a straight line rotating about an intersecting line generates a cone; a circle rotating about a diameter generates a sphere; a parabola rotating about its axis generates a paraboloid of revolution; an ellipse rotating about either axis generates an ellipsoid of revolution, or a spheroid. The corresponding solids are called **solids of revolution.**

5·10. The following example shows the method of finding by calculus the volume of a solid of revolution.

Example 2. Find the volume of a cone of height h which is generated by rotating the line $y=mx$ about the x-axis.

Let P(x, y) be a point on the line; draw PN the ordinate of P.

When the figure is rotated about the x-axis, let V be the volume between O and the plane generated by the rotation of PN.

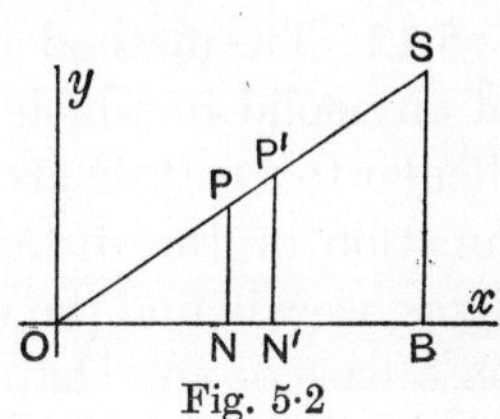

Fig. 5·2

Now let PN move to P′N′ and let Δx, Δy, ΔV be corresponding increments of x, y, V.

When NPP′N′ rotates about the x-axis it generates a disk with bevelled edges, the thickness of the disk being Δx and the areas of the parallel faces πy^2 and $\pi(y+\Delta y)^2$.

$$\therefore\ \Delta V \text{ lies between } \pi y^2 \Delta x \text{ and } \pi(y+\Delta y)^2 \Delta x.$$

$$\therefore\ \frac{\Delta V}{\Delta x} \text{ lies between } \pi y^2 \text{ and } \pi(y+\Delta y)^2.$$

Now as $\Delta x \to 0$, $\dfrac{\Delta V}{\Delta x} \to \dfrac{dV}{dx}$ and $\Delta y \to 0$.

$$\therefore\ \frac{dV}{dx} = \pi y^2 = \pi m^2 x^2.$$

$$\therefore\ V = \pi m^2 \frac{x^3}{3} + c.$$

When P is brought back to O, i.e. when $x=0$, V$=0$.

$$\therefore\ c=0.$$

When P moves to S, i.e. when $x=h$, V is the required volume.

$$\therefore\ \text{the required volume} = \tfrac{1}{3}\pi m^2 h^3.$$

Now $\mathsf{OB}=h$, $\mathsf{BS}=mh$.

$\therefore$ the volume of the cone $=\frac{1}{3}\pi m^2h^2.h = \frac{1}{3}\pi \mathsf{BS}^2.\mathsf{OB}$
$= \frac{1}{3}$ base area $\times$ height.

5·11. Note that the result $\frac{d}{dx}$(volume) $=\pi y^2$ applies to the volume generated by the rotation of a curve about the x-axis whatever function y is of x. Later on we may assume this result, but for the present it will be wise to put the work out fully as above.

Volume of a pyramid

5·12. The method of § 5·10 may be applied to finding the volume of any solid in which the area of the plane cross-section perpendicular to a certain straight line is a known function of the distance along that line. Thus, we will find the volume of a pyramid, on a base of any shape.

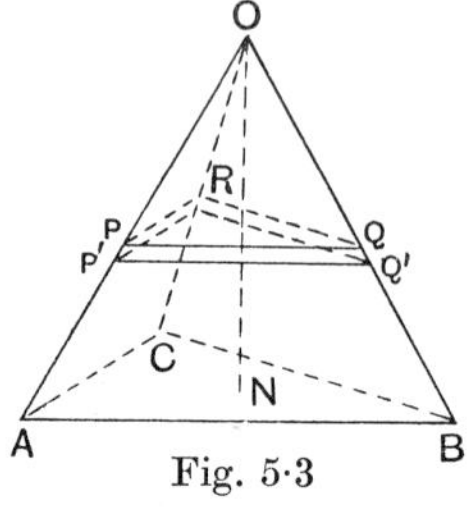

Fig. 5·3

Let the area of the base be S, and the height h.

Consider a plane section of the pyramid, parallel to the base, giving the figure PQR. This is a figure similar to the base.

Let the distance PQR from O be x units. The volume of the pyramid cut off by PQR is a function of x; let it be V.

Let PQR be moved parallel to itself to P′Q′R′, so that x is increased to $x+\Delta x$. The volume V is increased by the slice whose upper and lower faces are PQR, P′Q′R′: call this ΔV.

Now the volume of this slice is greater than that of a prism whose base is PQR and whose height is Δx. Similarly, the volume of the slice is less than that of a prism whose base is P′Q′R′ and whose height is Δx.

$\therefore$ ΔV lies between $\Delta x \times$ area PQR and $\Delta x \times$ area P′Q′R′,

$$\therefore \quad \frac{\Delta \mathsf{V}}{\Delta x} \text{ lies between area PQR and area P′Q′R′.}$$

Now, as $\Delta x \to 0$, $\frac{\Delta \mathsf{V}}{\Delta x} \to \frac{d\mathsf{V}}{dx}$, and area P′Q′R′ $\to$ area PQR.

$$\therefore \quad \frac{d\mathsf{V}}{dx} = \text{area of PQR.}$$

But PQR is similar to ABC; and the ratio of the linear dimensions is $x:h$.

$$\therefore \text{ area of PQR} = \frac{x^2}{h^2} \times \text{area of ABC}$$

$$= \frac{x^2}{h^2} \times \mathsf{S}.$$

$$\therefore \frac{d\mathsf{V}}{dx} = \frac{x^2}{h^2} \times \mathsf{S} = \frac{\mathsf{S}}{h^2} \times x^2.$$

Observing that $\frac{\mathsf{S}}{h^2}$ is a constant factor, we have

$$\mathsf{V} = \frac{1}{3}\frac{\mathsf{S}}{h^2} \times x^3 + c.$$

Now when $x=0$, $\mathsf{V}=0$, $\therefore c=0$.

$$\therefore \mathsf{V} = \frac{1}{3}\frac{\mathsf{S}x^3}{h^2}.$$

This gives the volume cut off from the pyramid by PQR. For the whole volume of the pyramid we make PQR coincide with ABC, and $x=h$.

$$\therefore \text{ volume of pyramid } = \tfrac{1}{3}\mathsf{S}h \text{ units of volume.}$$

Hence the important result that the volume of a pyramid is measured by one-third of the product of the base and height.

Exercise 5*g*

1. $y^2 = 4ax$ represents a parabola whose axis of symmetry is the x-axis. By rotating the curve about the x-axis, a paraboloid of revolution is formed. Of what form are sections of this surface made by planes perpendicular to the x-axis? Of what form are sections made by planes containing the x-axis? Find the volume bounded by the paraboloid and a plane perpendicular to the x-axis at $x=b$. Prove that this is half the volume of a circumscribing cylinder.

2. Find the volume cut off from the solid obtained by rotating the parabola $y^2=4ax$ about its axis by a plane at a distance $5a$ from its vertex.

3. $y^2 = c^2 - x^2$ represents a circle of radius c, with centre at the origin. What surface is formed by rotating this about the x-axis? Find the volume bounded by this surface, and planes perpendicular to the x-axis through $x=a$, $x=b$, where a and b are positive and $b>a$. What values must be given to a and b in order to deduce the volume of the hemisphere? What is this volume?

4. Find by integration the volume of a sphere of radius a.

A portion is cut off this sphere by a plane at a distance $\frac{1}{2}a$ from the centre. Show that the volume of this portion is $\frac{5}{32}$ of the volume of the sphere.

5. A cup, formed by part of a sphere of radius 5 in., contains water to a depth of 3 in. Find the volume of water.

6. $y^2 = 1-\dfrac{x^2}{4}$ represents an ellipse with centre at the origin, and longer axis along the x-axis. Find where the ellipse cuts the two axes, and hence make a rough sketch of the curve. Find the volume of the ellipsoid of revolution (prolate spheroid) formed by rotating this ellipse about its longer axis.

---

7. The ellipse $\dfrac{x^2}{a^2}+\dfrac{y^2}{b^2} = 1$ is revolved about the x-axis. Find the volume of the solid so formed.

8. Fig. 5·4 shows a part of the graph $y=\dfrac{1}{x}$. Find the volume generated by the rotation of APQB about the x-axis, where OA $=a$, OB $=b$. Show that as $b \to \infty$, this volume tends to a finite limit.

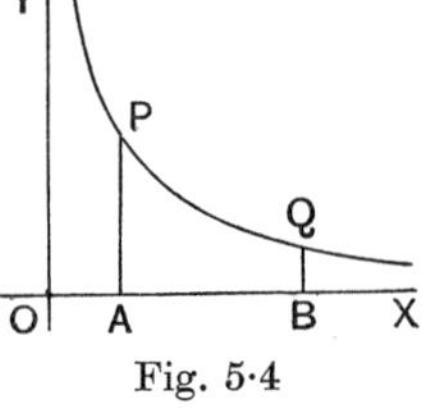

Fig. 5·4

9. Trace the hyperbola whose equation is

$$x^2-xy+a^2 = 0.$$

If the curve revolves about the axis of x, find the volume of the solid generated between the limits $x=a$ and $x=2a$.

10. Find the volume of the solid formed by the revolution about the axis of x of the curve $y^2 = x(a-x)$.

11. The shape of the head of a certain bullet is that formed by the revolution of part of a parabola about the axis of the parabola. If the total length of the head, measured from the vertex of the parabola, is 2·7 cm., and the diameter of the bullet is 0·6 cm., find the volume of the head.

[The equation of the parabola is $y^2=4ax$, with the tangent at the vertex as axis of y, and the vertex as origin.]

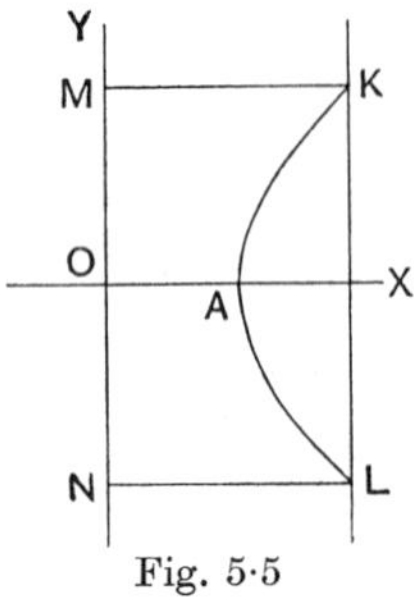

Fig. 5·5

12. Fig. 5·5 shows a portion of the rectangular hyperbola $x^2-y^2 = a^2$ cut off by a chord KL, parallel to OY at a distance $2a$ from OY. Show that the volume of the solid cap formed by the revolution of KAL about OX is equal to the volume of a sphere of radius a.

Show also that if the figure be rotated about the axis OY, the solid generated by the revolution of the figure MKALN has half the volume of the cylinder generated by the revolution of the rectangle MKLN.

13. The straight lines $y=2x$ and $y=5$ are made to revolve round the axis of y. Find the volume of the solid figure thus formed.

14. Draw (roughly) in one figure the curves $y = 1-x^2$, $y = 2-2x^2$. The area entirely enclosed between these curves is rotated about the axis of x. Find the volume of the solid thus generated.

15. The area included between the parts of the two curves $x^2+y^2 = 1$ and $4x^2+y^2 = 4$ for which y is positive is rotated about the axis of x. Find the volume of the solid thus formed.

---

16. A cylindrical hole of radius c is cut through a solid sphere of radius a, the axis of the cylinder coinciding with a diameter of the sphere. Show that the volume which is left is equal to that of a sphere of radius $\sqrt{(a^2-c^2)}$.

17. An equilateral triangle with unit sides is revolved about a line through one of its corners and parallel to the opposite side. Find the volume of the solid so formed.

---

18. A vessel for holding water is 10 in. deep, and the area, y sq.in., of the water surface when the depth of the water is x in. is given by the equation $y = 2+x+\frac{1}{2}x^2$. Find what volume of water it will hold.

19. A bath is of such dimensions that, when it is filled to a depth x ft., the area of the water surface is $\left(10+4x+\frac{x^2}{3}\right)$ sq.ft.

Find the number of gallons of water in the bath when it is filled to a depth of 2 ft., taking 1 cu.ft. = $6\frac{1}{4}$ gallons.

20. The shape of a hill is such that, at a height of x ft. above the foot of the hill, the horizontal section has an area of $20{,}000(100-x)$ sq.ft. Find the height of the hill by calculating the height at which the sectional area is zero; also find the number of cubic feet of earth in the hill.

---

21. The length of a submarine boat is $2a$ ft., and the vertical height of the hull is $2b$ ft. The area of a horizontal section, at a height of x ft. above the lowest point of the hull, is

$$\pi ab\left[1-\frac{(x-b)^2}{b^2}\right] \text{ sq.ft.}$$

Prove that the volume of the hull is $4\pi ab^2$ cu.ft.

22. The height of a beer barrel, standing on its end, is $2h$ ft., the radius of each end r ft., the radius of the greatest horizontal section R ft. (all inside

measurements); when the depth of beer in the barrel is x ft., the area of the surface of the beer in sq.ft. is

$$\pi\left\{\mathrm{R}^2-\frac{(\mathrm{R}^2-r^2)(x-h)^2}{h^2}\right\}.$$

Prove that the capacity of the barrel, in cu.ft., is

$$\frac{2\pi h}{3}(2\mathrm{R}^2+r^2).$$

CHAPTER 6

CO-ORDINATE GEOMETRY

Distance between two points

6·1. Example 1. Find the distance between the points (2, 3) and (6, 1).

A is (2, 3) and B is (6, 1).

Draw AL, BM $\perp$ Ox, and BN $\perp$ AL.

In the right-angled triangle ABN, since AB is the hypotenuse,

$$AB^2 = AN^2 + NB^2$$
$$= 2^2 + 4^2.$$
$$\therefore\ AB = \sqrt{(20)}$$
$$= 2\sqrt{5}.$$

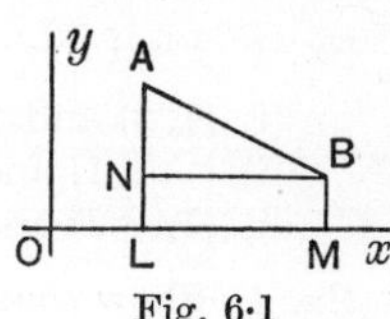

Fig. 6·1

Ex. 1. Find the distance between the pairs of points,

(i) (1, 2) and (5, 5).
(ii) (−2, −1) and (3, 11).
(iii) (−9, 4) and (15, −3).

The use of a suffix

6·2. It is frequently necessary to deal with several points whose co-ordinates are not known. In order to distinguish between them it is usual to write their co-ordinates in the form

$$(x_1, y_1),\quad (x_2, y_2),\quad \text{and so on.}$$

Care must be taken to write the numbers at the bottom of the letter (as a *suffix*) so that there is no confusion with an index.

[The suffix notation used in § 2·9 for $D_x(2x^2+t)$ has an entirely different meaning.]

Ex. 2. Show that the distance between the points (x_1, y_1) and (x_2, y_2) is

$$\sqrt{[(x_1-x_2)^2+(y_1-y_2)^2]}$$

(i) when both points are in the first quadrant,
(ii) when the two points are in different quadrants.

Mid-point of the line joining two given points

6·3. Example 2. Find the mid-point of the line joining $(-1, 3)$ and $(6, 5)$.

A is $(-1, 3)$ and B is $(6, 5)$. P(x, y) is the mid-point of AB. AL, PM, BN are all $\perp$ Ox.

Then LM = MN, and so $1 + x = 6 - x$.

$$\therefore \; x = \frac{6-1}{2} = \frac{5}{2}.$$

Similarly $y = 4$.

$\therefore$ P is the point $(\tfrac{2}{5}, 4)$.

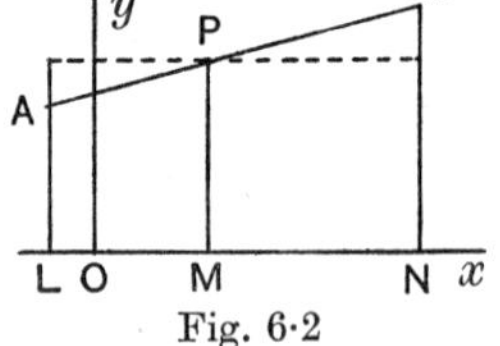

Fig. 6·2

Ex. 3. Find the mid-points of the following pairs of points:

(i) $(1, 2)$ and $(5, 5)$,
(ii) $(-2, 1)$ and $(3, -11)$,
(iii) $(1, -2)$ and $(4, 7)$.

Ex. 4. Show that the mid-point of the line joining (x_1, y_1) and (x_2, y_2) is

$$\left(\frac{x_1+x_2}{2}, \frac{y_1+y_2}{2}\right),$$

(i) when both points lie in the first quadrant,
(ii) when the two points lie in different quadrants.

Division of a line in a given ratio

6·4. Example 3. Find the co-ordinates of the point which divides the line joining $(-7, 1)$ and $(2, 6)$ in the ratio $5:3$.

A is $(-7, 1)$ and B is $(2, 6)$. P(x, y) divides AB internally in the ratio $5:3$. AL, PM and BN are all $\perp$ Ox.

By geometry, $\dfrac{\text{LM}}{\text{MN}} = \dfrac{\text{AP}}{\text{PB}} = \dfrac{5}{3}.$

The actual length of MO is $-x$, so that

$$\text{LM} = 7 - (-x)$$
$$= 7 + x,$$

and
$$\text{MN} = (-x) + 2$$
$$= 2 - x.$$

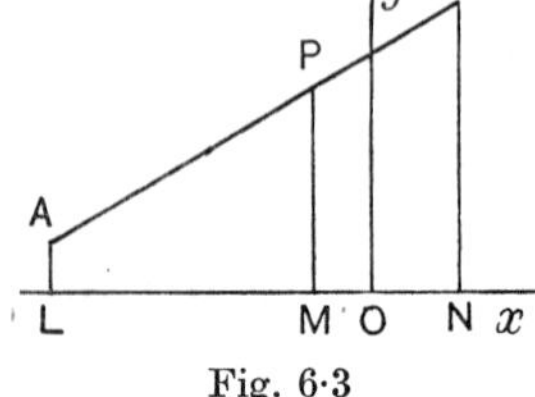

Fig. 6·3

$$\therefore \; \frac{7+x}{2-x} = \frac{5}{3}, \quad \text{or} \quad 21 + 3x = 10 - 5x.$$

$$\therefore \; 8x = 10 - 21, \quad \text{or} \quad x = -\tfrac{11}{8}.$$

Similarly, by drawing perpendiculars to Oy, we can show that

$$8y = 5(6) + 3(1), \quad \text{or} \quad y = \tfrac{33}{8}.$$

Hence P is the point $(-\tfrac{11}{8}, \tfrac{33}{8})$.

NOTE. If P divides AB *externally* in the ratio 5 : 3 we mean that P lies outside AB, on AB produced, so that

$$\frac{AP}{PB} = -\frac{5}{3}.$$

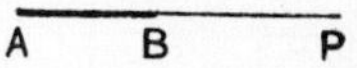

A B P

Fig. 6·4

If P divides AB externally in the ratio 3 : 5, then P lies on BA produced, and $\dfrac{AP}{PB} = -\dfrac{3}{5}$.

Ex. 5. Find the co-ordinates of the point P which divides AB internally in the given ratio:

(i) A(2, 3), B(5, 11), ratio 3 : 2.
(ii) A(−2, −3), B(5, 11), ratio 2 : 7.
(iii) A(x_1, y_1), B(x_2, y_2), ratio 5 : 4.

Ex. 6. Find the co-ordinates of the point P which divides AB externally in the given ratio:

(i) A(2, 3), B(6, 5), ratio 3 : 1.
(ii) A(2, 3), B(4, −3), ratio 1 : 2.
(iii) A(x_1, y_1), B(x_2, y_2), ratio 5 : 4.

Lines parallel to the axes

6·5. In fig. 6·5, it should be clear that the x of any point on MP is equal to a. In fact, the equation of the line MP is $x = a$.

Similarly, the equation of the line NP is $y = b$.

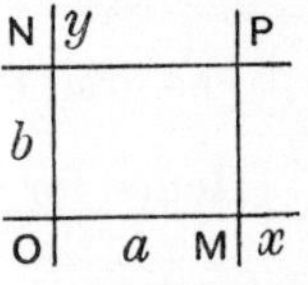

Fig. 6·5

Gradient of the line joining two given points

6·6. Example 4. Find the gradients of the lines joining:
(i) A (1, 2) and B (6, 5), (ii) C (−2, 3) and D (4, −1).

(i) The gradient of AB is

$$\frac{NB}{AN} = \frac{5-2}{6-1} = \frac{3}{5}.$$

(ii) Here the gradient of CD is negative. It is

$$\frac{\mathsf{MD}}{\mathsf{CM}}=\frac{-1-3}{4-(-2)}=\frac{-4}{6}=-\frac{2}{3}.$$

Note carefully the 'sense' or direction of CM and MD.

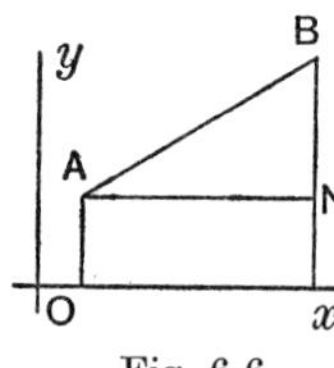

Fig. 6·6

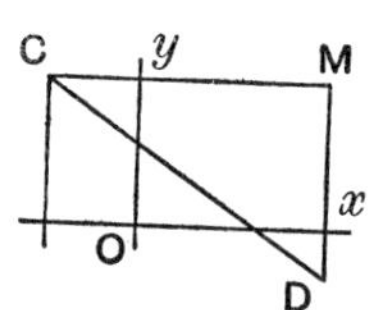

Fig. 6·7

Ex. 7. Find the gradient of the lines joining the pairs of points,

(i) (5, 6) and (3, 2), (ii) (3, 2) and (4, 3),
(iii) (−2, 3) and (4, −1), (iv) (−2, −1) and (2, 1),
(v) (−3, 2) and (4, 2), (vi) (3, −2) and (3, 4).

¶**Ex. 8.** Show that the gradient of the line joining (x, y) and (a, b) is $\dfrac{y-b}{x-a}$.
Is this result true for all positions of the two points?

Equation of the line through a given point and with a given gradient

6·7. Let A, (a, b), be the given point and m the given gradient. Let P, (x, y), be any point on the line.

The gradient of AP is $\dfrac{y-b}{x-a}$, and this is to be m.

Hence for all positions of P

$$\frac{y-b}{x-a}=m,$$

i.e. $$y-b=m(x-a).$$

This is the required equation.

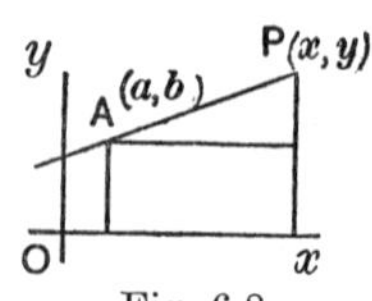

Fig. 6·8

Ex. 9. Find the equations of the lines

(i) through (3, 4) with gradient $\frac{1}{2}$,
(ii) through (−3, 2) with gradient −1,
(iii) through (5, −2) with gradient 2,
(iv) through (1, 2) with gradient $-\frac{3}{4}$.

¶ For discussion.

Equation of the line joining two points

6·8. Example 5. Find the equation of the line through A $(1, 2)$ and B $(6, 5)$.

See fig. 6·6.

The gradient of AB $= \dfrac{5-2}{6-1} = \dfrac{3}{5}$.

$\therefore$ the equation of AB is $y-2 = \frac{3}{5}(x-1)$, i.e. $3x-5y+7 = 0$.

Ex. 10. Could the equation of AB in Example 5 be written as

$$y-5 = \tfrac{3}{5}(x-6)\,?$$

Does this produce the same result?

Ex. 11. Find the equations of the lines joining the pairs of points given in Ex. 7.

Parallel lines

6·9. Parallel lines have the same gradient. For example,

(i) $y = 3x+2$ and $y = 3x-1$ have gradient 3 and are parallel,

(ii) $2x-3y+4 = 0$ and $4x-6y = 5$ have gradient $\frac{2}{3}$ and are parallel.

In general, the lines $y = m_1x+c_1$ and $y = m_2x+c_2$ are parallel if

$$m_1 = m_2.$$

Ex. 12. Find the equation of the line

(i) through $(3, 2)$ parallel to $3x-y+5 = 0$,

(ii) through $(-2, 1)$ parallel to $4x+3y = 7$,

(iii) through the origin parallel to $x-y+1 = 0$.

Ex. 13. Show that the four lines $y = 2x$, $3x+y = 5$, $2x-y+3 = 0$ and $3x+y = 7$ form a parallelogram.

Perpendicular lines

6·10. AB and BC are perpendicular lines. Figs. 6·9 and 6·10 show the angles which they make with Ox; in fig. 6·9 the gradient

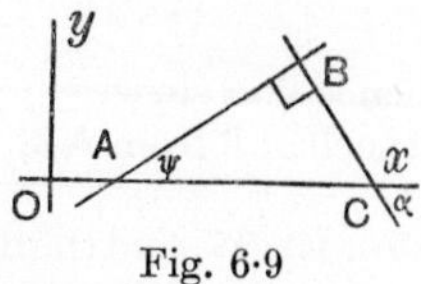

Fig. 6·9

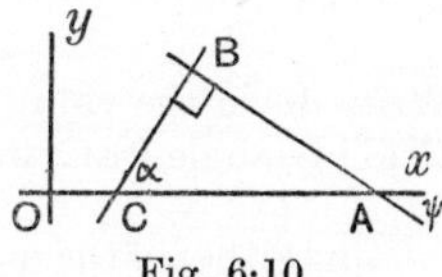

Fig. 6·10

of AB is $+\tan\psi$, and in fig. 6·10 it is $-\tan\psi$; in fig. 6·9 the gradient of BC is $-\tan\alpha$, and in fig. 6·10 it is $+\tan\alpha$. So in each figure the gradients of AB and BC have opposite signs.

In both figures $\psi+\alpha = 1$ right angle, so that

$$\tan\psi = \cot\alpha, \quad \text{or} \quad \tan\psi\tan\alpha = 1.$$

If m_1 is the gradient of AB and m_2 that of BC, it follows that

$$m_1(-m_2) = 1 \quad \text{or} \quad (-m_1)(m_2) = 1.$$

Hence lines with gradients m_1 and m_2 are perpendicular if

$$m_1 m_2 = -1.$$

If the gradient of a given line is m_1, the gradient of any perpendicular line is $-\dfrac{1}{m_1}$.

Ex. 14. Find the equation of the line

(i) through (3, 2) perpendicular to $3x-y+5 = 0$,
(ii) through $(-1, 2)$ perpendicular to $4x+3y = 7$,
(iii) through the origin perpendicular to $x-y = 1$.

Ex. 15. Show that the lines $2x-y+3 = 0$, $2x-y = 0$, $x+2y = 0$, $x+2y = 5$ form a rectangle.

Distance of a point from a line

6·11. Ex. 16. In fig. 6·11, P is the point (3, 7), and AB is the line $3x-4y = 6$.

(i) Find the equation of the line PB perpendicular to AB.
(ii) By solving the equations for AB, PB, find the co-ordinates of the point B.
(iii) Hence find the distance of P from AB.

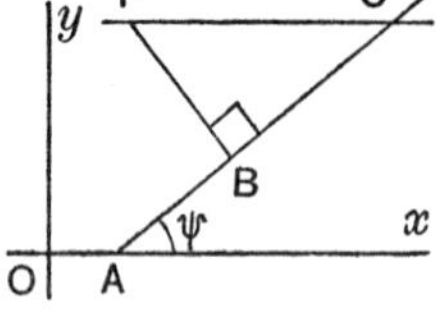

Fig. 6·11

Ex. 17. (i) In Ex. 16, if PC is parallel to Ox, find the co-ordinates of C and hence the length PC.

(ii) Write down the value of $\tan\psi$ and hence find $\sin\psi$.
(iii) Using triangle PBC, find PB, the distance of P from AB.

Ex. 18. Using either of the methods of Ex. 16 or Ex. 17, find the distance of

(i) (0, 7) from $4x-3y = 4$,
(ii) $(-1, 2)$ from $4x+3y = 7$,
(iii) the origin from $x-y = 1$,
(iv) (1, 2) from $5x+12y+10 = 0$.

The tangent and normal

6·12. In chapter 2 the gradient of a curve at any point is defined as the gradient of the tangent to the curve at this point, and this gradient is then found by the process of differentiation.

Example 6. Find the equation of the tangent to $y = 2x^2 - 3$ at the point $(2, 5)$.

Here $\dfrac{dy}{dx} = 4x$, so the gradient at $(2, 5)$ is 8.

The tangent is

$$y - 5 = 8(x-2), \quad \text{or} \quad 8x - y = 11.$$

The *normal* to a curve at a given point is the line passing through the point perpendicular to the tangent.

Example 7. Find the equation of the normal to the curve $xy = 6$ at the point $(2, 3)$.

$$y = \frac{6}{x}, \quad \therefore \frac{dy}{dx} = -\frac{6}{x^2}.$$

The gradient of the tangent at $(2, 3)$ is therefore $-\frac{6}{4}$, or $-\frac{3}{2}$.
The gradient of the normal is therefore $\frac{2}{3}$.
Hence the equation of the normal at $(2, 3)$ is

$$y - 3 = \tfrac{2}{3}(x-2),$$

or

$$2x - 3y + 5 = 0.$$

Ex. 19. Find the equations of the tangents and normals to the following curves at the points named:

(i) $y = 4x^2 - 3x$, $(2, 10)$.
(ii) $y = 4 + 5x - x^2$, where $x = 1$.
(iii) $xy = 12$, $(4, 3)$.
(iv) $xy + 14 = 0$, where $y = 7$.

The circle

In dealing with the circle it is best to use its geometrical properties.

6·13. Example 8. Find the equation of the circle with centre at (4, 5) and radius $2\frac{1}{2}$ units.

Let P(x, y) be any point on the circle, the centre of which is C. Then PC is always equal to $2\frac{1}{2}$ units.

$$\therefore\ (x-4)^2+(y-5)^2 = (2\tfrac{1}{2})^2.$$

This is the equation of the circle.

Example 9. Find the equation of the tangent and normal to the circle in the previous example at the point $(6, 6\frac{1}{2})$.

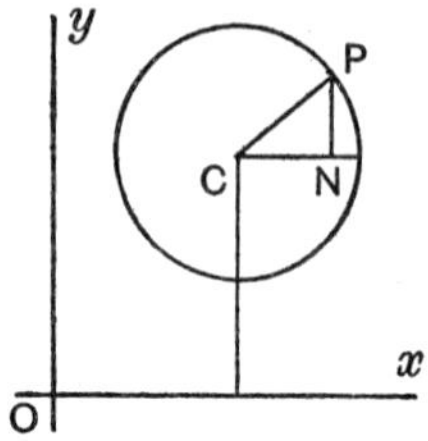

The normal is the radius through the given point, and is therefore the line joining $(6, 6\frac{1}{2})$ to $(4, 5)$.

Fig. 6·12

The gradient is $\dfrac{1\frac{1}{2}}{2} = \dfrac{3}{4}$.

The equation of the normal is therefore

$$y-5 = \tfrac{3}{4}(x-4), \quad \text{i.e.} \quad 3x-4y+8 = 0.$$

The gradient of the tangent is $-\frac{4}{3}$, and its equation is

$$y-6\tfrac{1}{2} = -\tfrac{4}{3}(x-6),$$

or

$$4x+3y = 43\tfrac{1}{2}.$$

Ex. 20. Find the equation of the circle with its centre at the origin and radius 5, and the equations of its tangent and normal at (3, 4).

Ex. 21. Find the equation of the circle with its centre at $(-3, 4)$ and radius 5, and the equations of the tangents and normals at the points at which $x=0$.

¶**Ex. 22.** What is the equation of the circle whose radius is r and centre (a, b)?

¶**Ex. 23.** Find the centre and radius of the circles whose equations are

(i) $x^2+y^2-2x-8y+8 = 0$, (ii) $x^2+y^2+6x-4y+12 = 0$.

Ex. 24. Find the equations of the tangents and normals to

$$x^2+y^2-2x-4y = 20$$

at the points where $x=4$.

¶ For discussion.

Symmetry about the axes of co-ordinates

6·14. If the point (a, b) lies on a curve which is symmetrical about the x-axis, then the point $(a, -b)$ must also lie on the curve. This is true of the following curves:

$$y^2 = 2x, \quad x^2+y^2 = 4, \quad x^2+3y^2+5x = 10,$$

$$x^2-y^2 = 2x, \quad y^2 = x+\frac{1}{x}, \quad 3x^2y^2+y^4 = 5x.$$

It will be seen that a curve is symmetrical about Ox when its equation contains only even powers of y.

If the point (a, b) lies on a curve which is symmetrical about the y-axis, then the point $(-a, b)$ must also lie on the curve. This will occur when the equation of the curve contains only even powers of x.

Symmetry about a line is sometimes called T-symmetry.

¶**Ex. 25.** Write down the equations of five curves which are symmetrical about the y-axis.

Ex. 26. Sketch the curves

$$y^2 = 2x, \quad x^2 = 9y, \quad (x-1)^2+y^2 = 4, \quad x^2+(y-2)^2 = 4,$$
$$y^2 = x(x-2), \quad y = x^2(x^2-4), \quad x = y^2-9y^4.$$

S-symmetry

6·15. Suppose P lies on a given curve and O is the origin. Produce PO to P′ so that PO = OP′. Then, if P′ also lies on the given curve, the curve is said to possess centro-symmetry or S-symmetry. The origin is said to be the centre of symmetry.

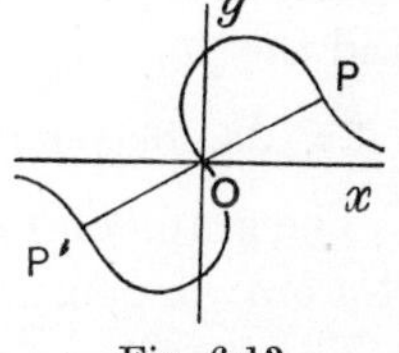

Fig. 6·13

If P is the point (a, b), then P′ is $(-a, -b)$. For the curve to possess S-symmetry with the origin as centre, the result of putting $x = a, y = b$ in its equation must be the same as that of putting $x = -a, y = -b$.

For example, the point (a, b) lies on the curve $x^2+2xy-3y^2 = 1$ when $a^2+2ab-3b^2 = 1$. The point $(-a, -b)$ also lies on the curve when this condition is fulfilled. Hence the curve has S-symmetry.

¶ For discussion.

Ex. 27. Which of the following curves has S-symmetry with the origin as centre? Which of them has symmetry about one of the axes of co-ordinates?

(i) $x^2+xy = 1$, (ii) $y = x^3-3x$,
(iii) $y^2 = x^3-3x$, (iv) $x^2+y^2 = 4$,
(v) $y = x(x-1)(x+1)$, (vi) $y^2 = x(x-1)(x+1)$.

The parabola

6·16. The equation $y = 3x^2-8x+5$ can be written

$$3x^2-8x+(5-y) = 0.$$

We can solve this for x in order to find those points on the curve $y = 3x^2-8x+5$ which have a given y co-ordinate. Thus,

$$x = \frac{8\pm\sqrt{\{64-12(5-y)\}}}{6},$$

or

$$x = \tfrac{4}{3}\pm\tfrac{1}{3}\sqrt{(3y+1)}.$$

This result shows that, when y is given, x has two values which are of the form

$$\tfrac{4}{3}\pm k.$$

The curve is therefore symmetrical about the line

$$x=\tfrac{4}{3}.$$

Also, since $(3y+1)$ must be positive, y cannot be less than $-\frac{1}{3}$.

Fig. 6·14 shows the curve $y=3x^2-8x+5$, which is called a **parabola**. It is *not* a closed curve.

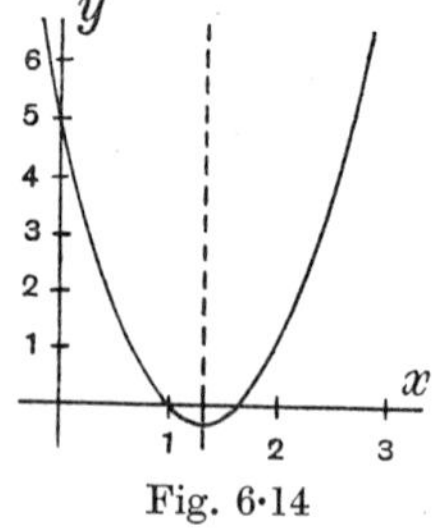

Fig. 6·14

The line of symmetry $x=\frac{4}{3}$ is called the axis of the parabola; and the point $(\frac{4}{3}, -\frac{1}{3})$ the vertex.

Ex. 28. Sketch the curve $y = 8x-3x^2-5$.

The graph of $y = ax^2+bx+c$ is discussed in Siddons and Daltry's *Algebra*, p. 246.

The function ax^2+bx+c is called the general quadratic function of x. Its graph is a parabola for all values of a, b and c $(a \neq 0)$. Solving the equation

$$ax^2+bx+(c-y) = 0,$$

we obtain

$$x = -\frac{b}{2a}\pm\frac{1}{2a}\sqrt{(4ay+b^2-4ac)},$$

so that the curve $y = ax^2 + bx + c$ is symmetrical about the line

$$x = -\frac{b}{2a}.$$

Again $$\frac{dy}{dx} = 2a\left(x + \frac{b}{2a}\right).$$

If a is positive the curve has a minimum when $x = -\dfrac{b}{2a}$.

If a is negative it has a maximum when $x = -\dfrac{b}{2a}$.

This is illustrated in fig. 6·15.

Ex. 29. Find the axes and vertices of the following parabolas and give freehand sketches of them:

(i) $y = x^2 - 6x + 5$, (ii) $y = 3 - x - x^2$,

(iii) $y = 2(x-1)(x-3)$, (iv) $2y = (3+x)(1-x)$.

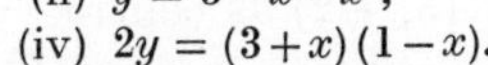

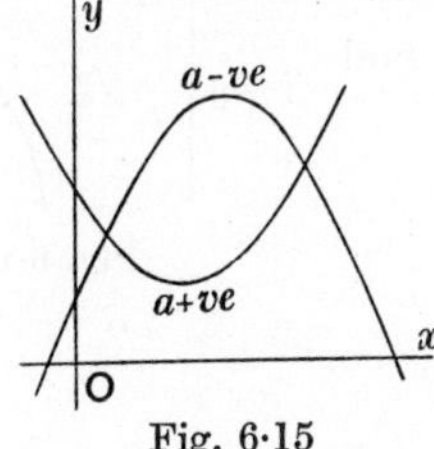

Fig. 6·15

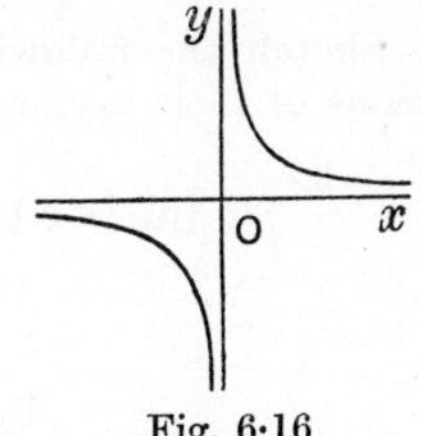

Fig. 6·16

The rectangular hyperbola

6·17. Graphs like $y = \dfrac{5}{x}$ and $y = \dfrac{2x}{x-3}$ have been discussed in Siddons and Daltry's *Algebra*, chapters 14 and 25.

Plotting a few points of $y = \dfrac{5}{x}$ tells us that it is not a closed curve, and introduces the difficulty of $x = 0$. The curve (see fig. 6·16) has no point corresponding to $x = 0$, but if x is numerically very small y is numerically very large. The curve gets nearer and nearer to the line $x = 0$ as it recedes from the origin, but there is no point of the curve actually lying on the line $x = 0$. Such a line is called an **asymptote** of the curve.

Similarly, by writing the equation in the form $x = \dfrac{5}{y}$, we see that $y = 0$ is also an asymptote.

If (a, b) lies on the curve, so does the point $(-a, -b)$, and the curve has S-symmetry with the origin as centre. The curve is called a **hyperbola.**

Example 10. Sketch the curve $y = \dfrac{2x}{3-x}$.

This curve has $x = 3$ as an asymptote.

Solving for x in terms of y we get

$$x = \frac{3y}{y+2}.$$

Thus $y = -2$ is also an asymptote.

The two asymptotes meet at $(3, -2)$, and we shall expect the curve to have S-symmetry with $(3, -2)$ as centre.

The curve is shown in fig. 6·17.

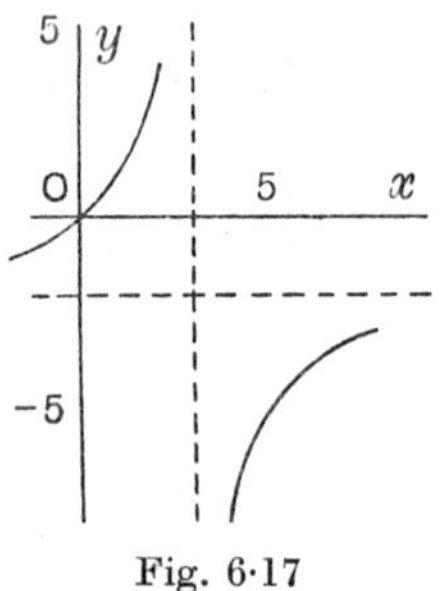

Fig. 6·17

Ex. 30. Sketch the following curves and find the equations of their asymptotes:

(i) $y = \dfrac{3x}{x-2}$, (ii) $(x+1)(y-2)+2 = 0$.

The ellipse

6·18. The curve $4x^2+9y^2 = 25$ is symmetrical about both axes. It cuts the axes at $(-\frac{5}{2}, 0)$, $(\frac{5}{2}, 0)$, $(0, -\frac{5}{3})$ and $(0, \frac{5}{3})$.

The equation can be written

$$x = \pm\tfrac{1}{2}\sqrt{(25-9y^2)},$$

so that y must lie between $-\frac{5}{3}$ and $+\frac{5}{3}$.

Similarly we can show that x must lie between $-\frac{5}{2}$ and $+\frac{5}{2}$.

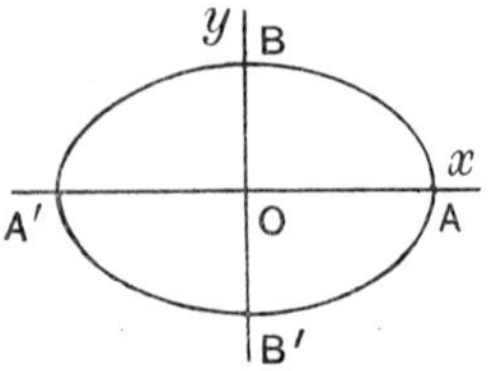

Fig. 6·18

The curve, shown in fig. 6·18, is a closed oval and is called an **ellipse.**

The equation $ax^2+by^2 = c$, where a, b and c are all positive, represents an ellipse which is symmetrical about both axes of co-ordinates. The longer axis of symmetry of the ellipse is known as the **major axis**, and the shorter axis of symmetry, the **minor axis**. Thus in fig. 6·18, A′A is the major axis and B′B is the minor axis of the ellipse $4x^2+9y^2 = 25$.

Note that a circle can be regarded as an ellipse which has its major and minor axes equal.

Ex. 31. Sketch the curve $\frac{x^2}{4}+\frac{y^2}{9}=1.$

What are the lengths of its major and minor axes?

The hyperbola referred to its axes

6·19. The curve $4x^2-9y^2 = 25$ is symmetrical about both axes. It cuts Ox at $(-\frac{5}{2}, 0)$ and $(\frac{5}{2}, 0)$, but it does not cut Oy.

Writing the equation in the form

$$x = \pm\tfrac{1}{2}\sqrt{(25+9y^2)},$$

we see that all values of y are possible. But when we solve for y,

$$y = \pm\tfrac{1}{3}\sqrt{(4x^2-25)},$$

and we see that x cannot lie between $-\frac{5}{2}$ and $+\frac{5}{2}$.

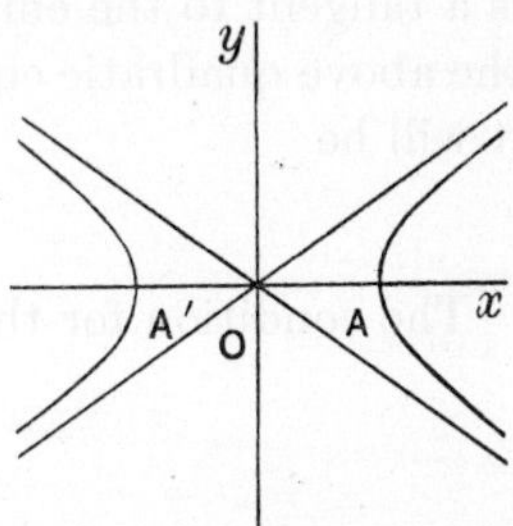

Fig. 6·19

We shall see later that the lines $2x+3y = 0$ and $2x-3y = 0$ are asymptotes of the curve, which is shown in fig. 6·19. The curve is a **hyperbola** and its asymptotes are inclined to one another at an angle $2\tan^{-1}\frac{2}{3}$. The hyperbolas considered in § 6·17 have their asymptotes at right angles to one another and so are called **rectangular hyperbolas.**

Ex. 32. Sketch the curve $4y^2-9x^2 = 25$.

Intersections of lines and curves

6·20. If a point P lies on two curves its co-ordinates satisfy the equations of both curves. These co-ordinates can therefore be found by solving the equations simultaneously.*

Example 11. Find the distance between the points in which the line $3x+y = 7$ cuts the circle $x^2+y^2-4y-1 = 0$.

Solving the equations of the line and the circle as simultaneous equations we find the points of intersection are

$$(1,4) \quad \text{and} \quad (2,1).$$

The length of the chord joining these two points is $\sqrt{5}$.

* See Siddons and Daltry, *Algebra*, p. 248.

Example 12. Find the values of c for which the line $x+2y = c$ is a tangent to the ellipse $4x^2+9y^2 = 1$.

The line meets the ellipse where

$$4(c-2y)^2+9y^2 = 1,$$

$$\text{i.e.} \quad 25y^2-16cy+4c^2-1 = 0.$$

In general this will give two intersections. When the line $x+27=c$ is a tangent to the ellipse there will be only one intersection, and the above quadratic equation must be a perfect square. Evidently it will be

$$\left(5y-\frac{8c}{5}\right)^2 = 0.$$

The condition for this is

$$\frac{64c^2}{25} = 4c^2-1,$$

$$\text{i.e.} \quad 36c^2 = 25, \quad \text{or} \quad c = \pm\tfrac{5}{6}.$$

The two tangents are therefore $x+2y = \frac{5}{6}$ and $x+2y+\frac{5}{6} = 0$.

Locus problems

6·21. If we require the locus of a point P which is constrained to move in a certain manner we suppose the co-ordinates of P to be (x, y). We then find an equation connecting x and y by using the conditions under which P is moving. From this equation the locus of P can be plotted, or its nature determined.

Example 13. A straight line cuts the axes of co-ordinates at Q and R, and it moves in such a way that the area of the triangle OQR is constant. If P is the point of trisection of QR which is nearer to Q, find the nature of the locus of P.

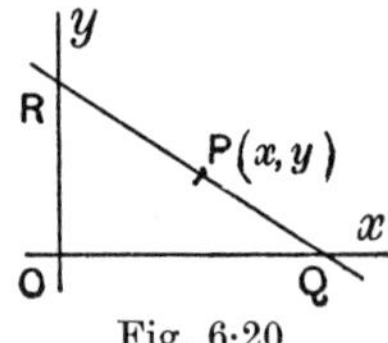

Fig. 6·20

Suppose Q is $(h, 0)$ and R is $(0, k)$. Then $hk=2\text{A}$, where A is the constant area.

Let P be the point (x, y), so that

$$x=\tfrac{2}{3}h, \quad y=\tfrac{1}{3}k.$$

From these equations, $h=\frac{3x}{2}$, $k=3y$. But $hk=2\mathsf{A}$,

$$\therefore \quad \frac{9xy}{2}=2\mathsf{A},$$

$$\text{or} \quad xy=\tfrac{4}{9}\mathsf{A}.$$

This is the equation of the locus of P, which is therefore a hyperbola.

Exercise 6*a*

1. The points A$(-3,4)$, B$(4,6)$ and C$(-1,-3)$ are the vertices of a triangle. Prove that it is right-angled and isosceles and find at which vertex the right angle is situated.

Find the co-ordinates of the mid-point of the hypotenuse.

2. The points A$(-7,1)$, B$(-1,3)$ and C$(-3,5)$ are the vertices of a triangle, F is the mid-point of AB and E is the mid-point of AC. Find:

(i) the co-ordinates of E and F;
(ii) the equations of EF and BC; verify that they are parallel;
(iii) the equation of AX, the perpendicular from A on BC.

3. The points A$(-8,3)$, B$(4,5)$ and C$(2,-1)$ are three of the vertices of a parallelogram ABCD. Calculate the co-ordinates of X, the mid-point of the diagonal AC, and those of D. Verify your result by calculating the gradients of opposite sides.

4. A is the point $(1,3)$ and BC the line whose equation is $2x-y+6=0$. Find the equations of the lines through A (i) parallel to BC, and (ii) perpendicular to BC. (iii) Find the point of intersection of the latter with BC and deduce the perpendicular distance of the point $(1,3)$ from BC.

5. Calculate the area of the triangle formed by the line $2x+3y=7$ with the axes. Find the equation of the line through the origin which divides the triangle into two parts equal in area.

6. Plot roughly the points A$(2,1)$, B$(4,6)$, C$(1,5)$; draw AD, BE, CF perpendicular to the x-axis. Find the area of triangle ABC by considering the areas of the three trapezia in the figure.

---

7. Find the equations of:

(i) the straight line joining $(5,1)$ and $(13,-3)$;
(ii) the straight line through $(-1,4)$ parallel to the line $2y=3x+10$;
(iii) the straight line joining the origin to the intersection of the lines $y=3x+4$ and $7y+8x=16$.

8. The points A$(-3,8)$ and C$(1,-2)$ are the opposite corners of the square ABCD. Find the equation of the diagonal BD and the co-ordinates of B and D.

9. Find the equations of the three medians of the triangle formed by the lines $3y = 5x$, $y = 7x$ and $x + y = 16$.

Prove that the medians meet at a point, and calculate its co-ordinates.

10. Find the length of the perpendicular from the point $(-1, 3)$ on the straight line $4x - 3y + 8 = 0$.

Find also the equation of the circle with centre $(-1, 3)$ touching this line.

11. The points $(2, 1)$, $(1, 5)$, $(4, 6)$ are the middle points of the sides of a triangle. Find the equations of the sides.

12. Find the area of the triangle whose vertices are $(-2, 1)$, $(6, 3)$ and $(3, 7)$.

---

13. Find the equations of the tangents to the curve

$$y = x^3 - 6x^2 + 12x - 1$$

at the points where $x = 2$ and $x = 3$.

Has y either a maximum or a minimum value at the point where $x = 2$?

14. Find the gradient of the curve $y = 4x^2 - 7x + 5$ at each of the points where it is cut by the line $y = 2$.

Find the equations of the tangents at these points and show that they meet on the straight line $15x = 7y$.

15. Find the equation of the normal to the parabola $y = 4x^2$ at the point $(t, 2t)$. Find where the normal cuts the line $x = 0$, and show that the distance from the origin exceeds $2t$ by a fixed length. Show in a figure what length is proved constant.

16. Find the points of intersection with the parabola $y = 3x^2 + 2$ of the lines (i) $y = 6x + 11$, (ii) $y = 6x - 1$. Interpret the result of (ii).

17. Find the value of c such that $x - y = c$ is a tangent to $y^2 = 4x$. What are the co-ordinates of the point of contact?

18. The equation $x + 2 = ay$ represents a straight line through $(-2, 0)$. Find the values of a for which it is a tangent to the parabola $y^2 = 8x$. Hence find the equation of the two tangents from $(-2, 0)$ to the parabola and show that they are at right angles to one another.

19. Find the equation of the tangent to the hyperbola $xy = 1$ at the point $\mathsf{P}\left(t, \frac{1}{t}\right)$.

If the tangent cuts the axes of co-ordinates at A and B, show that AP = PB.

---

20. Find the slopes of the tangents at the points $(-1, 0)$, $(1, 0)$, $(3, 0)$ to the curve

$$y = k(x^3 - 3x^2 - x + 3).$$

Show that the tangents at $(-1, 0)$ and $(3, 0)$ are parallel, and find k so that the tangent at $(1, 0)$ may be at right angles to the other two.

21. Find the equation of the normal to the parabola $x^2 = 4y$ at the point $(4, 4)$.

Find also the co-ordinates of the point at which this normal meets the parabola again, and show that the length of the chord so formed is $5\sqrt{5}$.

22. Show that $y = 2ax - a^2 + 3$ is the equation of the tangent to the curve $y = x^2 + 3$ at the point $(a, a^2 + 3)$.

Hence find the co-ordinates of the two points on the curve, the tangents at which pass through the point $(2, 6)$.

23. Find the equations of the two tangents to the hyperbola $xy = 27$ which are perpendicular to the straight line $4x - 3y = 7$. Also find the points of contact of these tangents.

24. Find the gradient of the hyperbola $xy = 1$ at the point $(2, \frac{1}{2})$.

Find the numerical values of A and B which make the parabola

$$4y = x^2 + Ax + B$$

pass through the point $(2, \frac{1}{2})$ and touch the hyperbola at that point.

25. A and B are two points on the parabola $x^2 = 16y$ and C is the mid-point of AB. The equation of the line AB is $4y - x - 24 = 0$. Find the co-ordinates of C.

The line CD is drawn parallel to the axis of the parabola to cut the parabola at the point D. Find the equation of the tangent at D and show that it is parallel to AB.

---

26. Find the equation of the locus of points equidistant from the points $(-1, 3)$ and $(2, 4)$.

Find the co-ordinates of the point equidistant from the points $(-1, 3)$, $(2, 4)$ and $(1, 2)$.

27. Find the centre and radius of the circle $x^2 - 6x + y^2 + 4y = 12$, and hence find the equation of the normal at the point $(6, -6)$ and the point at which the normal cuts the circle again.

28. Find the equation of the locus of a point which moves so that its distance from the point $(1, 0)$ is equal to its distance from the line $x + 1 = 0$.

Find the points at which the line $y = x - 3$ meets the locus, and prove that it is a normal at one of them.

29. Prove that the circles $x^2 + y^2 + 3x - y = 0$ and $x^2 + y^2 + x - 7y + 10 = 0$ are equal and that they touch each other.

30. Find the equation of the circle which has the points $(1, -10)$ and $(5, -8)$ as the ends of a diameter.

Prove that the straight line $2x - y = 20$ touches this circle.

31. Find the centre and radius of the circle $x^2 + y^2 - 2x - 14y + 25 = 0$. Hence find the length of the tangent to the circle from the origin.

32. A and B are two points on OX and OY respectively. If $OA = a$ and $OB = b$, what are the co-ordinates of P, the mid-point of AB?

If the line AB moves so that the area of the triangle OAB is always $2c^2$, find the locus of P.

Show that the line AB touches the locus at P.

33. The circle $x^2 + y^2 - 2x - 4y = 0$ passes through the origin. Find the co-ordinates of the other end of the diameter through the origin, and the co-ordinates of the point on the circle farthest from the y-axis.

34. $A(0, 0)$ and $B(a, a)$ are two fixed points. $P(x, y)$ is any point such that $PB = 3PA$. Find the equation of the locus of P and show that the locus is a circle.

Find the radius of the circle and the co-ordinates of its centre C. Show that A, B, C lie on a straight line.

35. Find the equation of the circle which has the points $(3, -1)$, $(1, 3)$ as extremities of a diameter.

Find the co-ordinates of the extremities of the perpendicular diameter.

CHAPTER 7

DIFFERENTIATION

7·1. The word 'Calculus' is derived from a Latin word meaning a little pebble; pebbles were used for doing sums.

The Calculus is a mathematical process, invented in the seventeenth century by Newton and Leibniz, which has revolutionized scientific development.

In earlier chapters of this book you have been introduced to two basic ideas: (i) differentiation for finding gradients and rates of change, (ii) integration, as anti-differentiation, for finding areas and volumes and distances travelled. But you have only applied these ideas to simple functions involving a few powers of x. In the last two chapters you will consider the third basic idea of the calculus, integration as a process of summation, and the differentiation and integration of more difficult algebraic functions, and so widen considerably the scope for applications.

7·2. The derived function of a function of x, $f(x)$, is defined as follows:

If a small increment Δx is made in the value of x, there will be a corresponding increment in the value of $f(x)$. The **derived function** or **derivative** of $f(x)$ is the limiting value, as $\Delta x \to 0$, of the fraction

$$\frac{\text{increment of } f(x)}{\text{increment of } x},$$

or, in symbols, $$\frac{d}{dx}f(x) = \lim_{\Delta x \to 0} \frac{f(x+\Delta x)-f(x)}{\Delta x}.$$

$\frac{d}{dx}f(x)$ is sometimes written $f'(x)$. It is also called the **differential coefficient** of $f(x)$.

Ex. 1. Differentiate, from first principles, x^3.

Ex. 2. Differentiate, from first principles, $\sqrt{x}$.

[Note that $\dfrac{\sqrt{(x+\Delta x)}-\sqrt{x}}{\Delta x} = \dfrac{\{\sqrt{(x+\Delta x)}-\sqrt{x}\}\{\sqrt{(x+\Delta x)}+\sqrt{x}\}}{\Delta x\{(\sqrt{(x+\Delta x)}+\sqrt{x})\}} = \ldots$]

Differentiation of x^n

7·3. (i) *When n is a positive integer.*

Let $y = x^n$, and let Δx, Δy be corresponding increments of x, y. Then

$$y + \Delta y = (x+\Delta x)^n.$$

$$\therefore \quad \frac{\Delta y}{\Delta x} = \frac{(x+\Delta x)^n - x^n}{\Delta x}$$

$$= \frac{1}{\Delta x}\left\{x^n\left(1+\frac{\Delta x}{x}\right)^n - x^n\right\}$$

$$= \frac{x^n}{\Delta x}\left\{1+n\frac{\Delta x}{x}+\frac{n(n-1)}{1.2}\left(\frac{\Delta x}{x}\right)^2+\ldots+\left(\frac{\Delta x}{x}\right)^n - 1\right\}$$

$$= x^{n-1}\left\{n+\frac{n(n-1)}{1.2}\frac{\Delta x}{x}+\text{terms of higher degree in }\frac{\Delta x}{x}\right\}.$$

$$\therefore \quad \frac{dy}{dx} = \lim_{\Delta x \to 0}\frac{\Delta y}{\Delta x} = nx^{n-1}.$$

$$\therefore \quad \boldsymbol{\frac{d}{dx}x^n = nx^{n-1}}.$$

Ex. 3. Read off the derivatives of (i) x^3, (ii) x^2, (iii) x^7.

(ii) *When n is not a positive integer.*

It is also true that $\frac{d}{dx}x^n = nx^{n-1}$ when n is any real number, positive or negative.

We shall assume it in examples here. It is proved in § 7·11 for rational values of n.

Example 1. *Differentiate* $\sqrt{x}$.

$$\sqrt{x} = x^{\frac{1}{2}}.$$

$$\therefore \quad \frac{d}{dx}\sqrt{x} = \tfrac{1}{2}x^{-\frac{1}{2}} = \frac{1}{2\sqrt{x}}.$$

Note that $\sqrt{x}$ denotes the positive square root of x.

Ex. 4. Read off the derivatives of

(i) $\sqrt{x^3}$, (ii) x^{-2}, (iii) $x^{-\frac{3}{2}}$, (iv) $\frac{1}{\sqrt{x}}$, (v) $\frac{1}{x^6}$,

(vi) $\sqrt{\frac{2}{x^3}}$, (vii) $\frac{1}{4x^2}$, (viii) $\sqrt{(3x)}$, (ix) $\frac{\sqrt[4]{x}}{4}$.

Integration of x^n

7·4. Regarding integration as a process of anti-differentiation, we see that since

$$\frac{d}{dx}x^n = nx^{n-1},$$

the integral of x^{n-1} is $\frac{1}{n}x^n + c$, and the integral of x^n is $\frac{1}{n+1}x^{n+1} + c$, where c is a constant; thus

$$\int x^n\,dx = \frac{x^{n+1}}{n+1} + c.$$

This last result is true for all values of n, except -1. This exception is dealt with in Part II.

Note that the easiest way to think of this is to increase the index by one, and then, by differentiating what has been obtained, to find the appropriate number by which to divide.

Example 2. *Integrate* $\sqrt{x}$.

$$\sqrt{x} = x^{\frac{1}{2}}.$$

$\therefore$ the integral of $x^{\frac{1}{2}}$ is $x^{\frac{3}{2}} \div \frac{3}{2} + c = \frac{2}{3}\sqrt{x^3} + c.$

Ex. 5. Read off the integrals of

(i) $\frac{1}{\sqrt{x}}$, (ii) x^{-2}, (iii) $\frac{1}{x^3}$, (iv) $5\sqrt{x^3}$, (v) $8\sqrt[3]{x}$.

Differentiation of a sum

7·5. In Chapter 2 we differentiated ax^2+bx+c. The same method applies to the sum or difference of a number of terms.

Let $y=u+v+w$, where u, v, w are functions of x.

With the usual notation,

$$y+\Delta y = u+\Delta u+v+\Delta v+w+\Delta w.$$

$$\therefore\ \Delta y = \Delta u+\Delta v+\Delta w.$$

$$\therefore\ \frac{\Delta y}{\Delta x} = \frac{\Delta u}{\Delta x}+\frac{\Delta v}{\Delta x}+\frac{\Delta w}{\Delta x}.$$

As $$\Delta x \to 0, \quad \frac{\Delta u}{\Delta x} \to \frac{du}{dx}, \text{ etc.}$$

$$\therefore \quad \frac{d}{dx}(u+v+w) = \frac{du}{dx}+\frac{dv}{dx}+\frac{dw}{dx}.$$

This assumes that the limit of a sum is equal to the sum of the limits.

Function of a function

7·6. Example 3. *Differentiate* $\sqrt{(3x+4)}$.

Let $3x+4 = u$ and let $y = \sqrt{(3x+4)} = \sqrt{u}$.

Now $$\frac{dy}{du} = \tfrac{1}{2}u^{-\frac{1}{2}} \quad \text{and} \quad \frac{du}{dx} = 3.$$

It seems likely that

$$\frac{dy}{dx} = \frac{dy}{du} \times \frac{du}{dx}$$

$$= \tfrac{1}{2}u^{-\frac{1}{2}} \times 3 = \frac{3}{2\sqrt{(3x+4)}}.$$

Ex. 6. Use the above method to differentiate (i) $(x^3)^2$, (ii) $(x^3+1)^2$, and verify by multiplying out first and then differentiating.

This method is justified in general by the following:
Let $y = f(u)$ and $u = \phi(x)$.
Let Δx, Δy, Δu be corresponding increments of x, y, u.

Now $$\frac{\Delta y}{\Delta x} = \frac{\Delta y}{\Delta u} \times \frac{\Delta u}{\Delta x}.$$

As $\Delta x \to 0$, so $\Delta u \to 0$.

Thus, in the limit, $$\frac{dy}{dx} = \frac{dy}{du} \times \frac{du}{dx}.$$

This assumes that the limit of a product is the product of the limits of the individual factors.

Ex. 7. If a car is moving with a velocity v when at a distance x from a fixed point, show that its acceleration is $v\,\dfrac{dv}{dx}$.

Ex. 8. For a stone thrown downwards, it is observed that the velocity, when the stone has fallen a distance x, is given by $v^2 = 16+64x$. Find the value of the acceleration, $v\dfrac{dv}{dx}$.

$\left[\text{Note that } \dfrac{d}{dx}v^2 = \dfrac{d}{dv}v^2 \times \dfrac{dv}{dx} = 2v\dfrac{dv}{dx}.\right]$

Example 4. *Differentiate* $(4-3x^5)^3$.

Let $u = 4-3x^5$. $\therefore \dfrac{du}{dx} = -3\times 5x^4 = -15x^4$.

Let $y = (4-3x^5)^3 = u^3$.

$$\therefore \frac{dy}{du} = 3u^2.$$

$$\begin{aligned}\therefore \frac{dy}{dx} &= \frac{dy}{du}\times\frac{du}{dx}\\ &= 3u^2\times(-15x^4)\\ &= -45x^4(4-3x^5)^2.\end{aligned}$$

After a little practice it should be possible to write this down without using u. Thus:

$$\begin{aligned}\frac{d}{dx}(4-3x^5)^3 &= 3(4-3x^5)^2\times(-3\times 5x^4)\\ &= -45x^4(4-3x^5)^2.\end{aligned}$$

Example 5. *Integrate* $\sqrt{(5-2x)}$.

Since $\sqrt{(5-2x)} = (5-2x)^{\frac{1}{2}}$.

The integral of $\sqrt{(5-2x)} = (5-2x)^{\frac{3}{2}} \div \{\frac{3}{2}\times(-2)\}+c$

$$= -\tfrac{1}{3}\sqrt{(5-2x)^3}+c.$$

Exercise 7a

Differentiate Nos. 1–32.

1. x^5-2.
2. $2x^4-5x^2$.
3. $x^3+\dfrac{2}{x}$.
4. $x^{10}-5x^6$.
5. $(3x-5)^4$.
6. $(1-2x)^{10}$.
7. $(4x-1)^{-1}$.
8. $(ax+b)^n$.
9. $(x^2+1)^3$.
10. $(3x^2-5)^4$.
11. $(4-3x^3)^2$.
12. $(c-dx^3)^n$.

13. $\sqrt{(2x+3)}$. 14. $(4-5x)^{\frac{3}{2}}$. 15. $\dfrac{1}{\sqrt{(2-x)}}$. 16. $(a-bx)^{\frac{3}{2}}$.

17. $\sqrt[3]{(x^2-1)}$. 18. $(2x^3+3)^{-\frac{1}{3}}$. 19. $(x^4-2x^2)^{-\frac{1}{2}}$. 20. $(x^n+1)^r$.

---

21. $(5x-1)^{10}$. 22. $x^4-\dfrac{1}{x^2}$. 23. $\left(x-\dfrac{1}{x}\right)^3$. 24. $\dfrac{1}{(3x-5)^2}$.

25. $\sqrt{\dfrac{2}{x}}$. 26. $(x^2-1)^{\frac{3}{2}}$. 27. $(2x^2-x)^{-\frac{1}{2}}$. 28. $(4x^3+1)^5$.

29. $(ax^2-b)^4$. 30. $\dfrac{a}{\sqrt{(ax+b)}}$. 31. $(ax^2+b)^n$. 32. $(ax^2+bx+c)^{-n}$.

Integrate Nos. 33–56.

33. $2x^3-x$. 34. $4x^2+5$. 35. $2-\dfrac{1}{x^2}$. 36. $2x+\dfrac{3}{x^2}$.

37. $(2x-3)^3$. 38. $(1-3x)^5$. 39. $(1-5x)^{-2}$. 40. $(ax+b)^{-n}$.

41. $\dfrac{1}{\sqrt{(2x+3)}}$. 42. $\sqrt[3]{(x-5)}$. 43. $(3x+2)^{\frac{3}{2}}$. 44. $(2-5x)^{-\frac{8}{3}}$.

---

45. $\sqrt{(3x-4)}$. 46. $(3x-4)^{10}$. 47. $(2-7x)^3$. 48. $(3+5x)^{\frac{1}{3}}$.

49. $\sqrt{x}-1$. 50. $\dfrac{1}{(2x-5)^3}$. 51. $\dfrac{1}{\sqrt[4]{(3x-4)}}$. 52. $\dfrac{1}{\sqrt{x}}-\dfrac{1}{x^4}$.

53. $\dfrac{x}{\sqrt{(x^2+1)}}$. 54. $x^2\sqrt{(x^3-2)}$. 55. $x^9\sqrt{(x^{10}+1)}$. 56. $x\sqrt{(3x^2-4)}$.

---

57. If $y^2 = 6x^2-3x$, find the value of $\dfrac{dy}{dx}$ at the point $(-1, 3)$.

58. Find at what point of the parabola $y^2 = 4x$ the gradient is 1.

59. In the circle $x^2+y^2 = 4$, find the gradient at the point $(1, -\sqrt{3})$.

60. If $y = \sqrt{(2x+4)}$, show that $y\dfrac{dy}{dx}$ is constant.

61. A stone, set sliding along ice, has a velocity v ft./sec. after travelling a distance x ft. given by $v^2 = 600-10x$. Find its retardation.

62. A mass set oscillating at the end of a spring is found to have a velocity v ft./sec. when the spring is compressed x ft. given by $v^2 = 100-400x^2$. Find its acceleration when it is instantaneously at rest.

Differentiation of a product

7·7. Let $y = u \times v$.

With the usual notation,

$$y + \Delta y = (u + \Delta u)(v + \Delta v)$$

$$= uv + v\Delta u + u\Delta v + \Delta u\,\Delta v.$$

$$\therefore \quad \Delta y = v\Delta u + u\Delta v + \Delta u\,\Delta v.$$

$$\therefore \quad \frac{\Delta y}{\Delta x} = v\frac{\Delta u}{\Delta x} + u\frac{\Delta v}{\Delta x} + \frac{\Delta u}{\Delta x} \times \Delta v.$$

$$\therefore \quad \frac{dy}{dx} = v\frac{du}{dx} + u\frac{dv}{dx} + \frac{du}{dx} \times 0.$$

$$\therefore \quad \boldsymbol{\frac{d}{dx}(uv) = v\frac{du}{dx} + u\frac{dv}{dx}}.$$

Ex. 9. Differentiate $x \times x^2$ and compare the result with $\dfrac{dx^3}{dx}$.

Ex. 10. Differentiate $(x^2+3)(x-5)$ as a product. Also multiply out the given expression and differentiate term by term.

Ex. 11. Differentiate:

(i) $x^2(x-1)^3$, (ii) $x\sqrt{(x+1)}$, (iii) $(x+1)^3(x-1)^2$, (iv) $\dfrac{1}{x}(2x+3)^{\frac{3}{2}}$.

The above may be extended to the product of 3 or more functions.

Let $y = uvw = u \times vw$.

$$\frac{dy}{dx} = vw\frac{du}{dx} + u\frac{d}{dx}(vw)$$

$$= vw\frac{du}{dx} + u\left(w\frac{dv}{dx} + v\frac{dw}{dx}\right)$$

$$= vw\frac{du}{dx} + uw\frac{dv}{dx} + uv\frac{dw}{dx}.$$

Differentiation of a quotient

7·8. Let $y = \dfrac{u}{v}$.

$$y + \Delta y = \frac{u + \Delta u}{v + \Delta v}.$$

$$\therefore\ \Delta y = \frac{u + \Delta u}{v + \Delta v} - \frac{u}{v}$$

$$= \frac{v(u + \Delta u) - u(v + \Delta v)}{v(v + \Delta v)}$$

$$= \frac{v\,\Delta u - u\,\Delta v}{v(v + \Delta v)}.$$

$$\therefore\ \frac{\Delta y}{\Delta x} = \frac{v\dfrac{\Delta u}{\Delta x} - u\dfrac{\Delta v}{\Delta x}}{v(v + \Delta v)}.$$

$$\therefore\ \boldsymbol{\frac{d}{dx}\left(\frac{u}{v}\right) = \frac{v\dfrac{du}{dx} - u\dfrac{dv}{dx}}{v^2}}.$$

This result may also be found as follows.

$$\frac{d}{dx}\left(\frac{u}{v}\right) = \frac{d}{dx}\left(u \times \frac{1}{v}\right)$$

$$= \frac{1}{v}\frac{du}{dx} + u\frac{d}{dv}\left(\frac{1}{v}\right) \times \frac{dv}{dx}$$

$$= \frac{1}{v}\frac{du}{dx} + u \times \frac{-1}{v^2}\frac{dv}{dx}$$

$$= \frac{v\dfrac{du}{dx} - u\dfrac{dv}{dx}}{v^2}.$$

This method may be applied to examples instead of remembering the formula.

Example 6. *Differentiate* $\dfrac{x^2-1}{x^2+1}$.

$$\frac{d}{dx}\left(\frac{x^2-1}{x^2+1}\right) = \frac{(x^2+1)\dfrac{d}{dx}(x^2-1)-(x^2-1)\dfrac{d}{dx}(x^2+1)}{(x^2+1)^2}$$

$$= \frac{(x^2+1)\,2x-(x^2-1)\,2x}{(x^2+1)^2}$$

$$= \frac{4x}{(x^2+1)^2}.$$

Ex. 12. Differentiate

(i) $\dfrac{2x-3}{3x+2}$, (ii) $\dfrac{5+3x}{3-5x}$, (iii) $\dfrac{x^2+1}{x-1}$,

(iv) $\dfrac{3x}{x^2+1}$, (v) $\dfrac{\sqrt{x}}{x^2-2}$, (vi) $\dfrac{2x-1}{\sqrt{x^3}}$.

Ex. 13. Differentiate $\dfrac{x-2}{(3x-4)^3}$, treating it as the product $(x-2)\times\dfrac{1}{(3x-4)^3}$.

Ex. 14. If $y = \sqrt{x}$, then $x = y^2$. Find $\dfrac{dy}{dx}$ and $\dfrac{dx}{dy}$.

Does $\dfrac{dy}{dx} = \dfrac{1}{\dfrac{dx}{dy}}$?

Ex. 15. Repeat Ex. 14 for $2y = \sqrt[3]{x}$.

Explicit and Implicit Functions

7·9. If y is given in terms of x, say $y = f(x)$, we speak of y as an **explicit function** of x. In such a case it may be possible to find x as an explicit function of y, as in Exx. 14 and 15.

But consider $y = 2x^3 - x$; here y is an explicit function of x, but we cannot express x as an explicit function of y, yet the equation implies that x is a function of y. We say that x is an **implicit function** of y.

Again, in $x^2 - 3xy + 2y^2 - y = 1$, y is an implicit function of x, and x is an implicit function of y.

$\dfrac{dy}{dx}$ and $\dfrac{dx}{dy}$

7·10. In Exx. 14, 15, we have seen how to find $\dfrac{dy}{dx}$ and $\dfrac{dx}{dy}$. But let us consider a case such as $y = 2x^3 - x$ in which x is an implicit function of y.

With the usual notation

$$\frac{\Delta x}{\Delta y} = 1 \div \frac{\Delta y}{\Delta x}.$$

Hence, as $\Delta x \to 0$, $\Delta y \to 0$, and assuming the appropriate limit theorem, $\dfrac{dx}{dy} = 1 \div \dfrac{dy}{dx}$, provided $\dfrac{dy}{dx} \neq 0$.

Now, as $y = 2x^3 - x$,

$$\therefore \quad \frac{dy}{dx} = 6x^2 - 1.$$

$$\therefore \quad \frac{dx}{dy} = \frac{1}{6x^2 - 1}.$$

But in using this we must be careful to see that the $\dfrac{dy}{dx}$ and $\dfrac{dx}{dy}$ apply to the same point on the curve.

If $y = x^2$, $\quad \dfrac{dx}{dy} = \dfrac{1}{2x} = \pm \dfrac{1}{2\sqrt{y}}$.

The graph of $y = x^2$ in fig. 7·1 shows why, for a given value of y, there are two values for $\dfrac{dx}{dy}$.

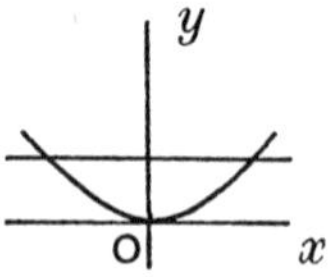

Fig. 7·1.

Ex. 16. Find $\dfrac{dx}{dy}$ in terms of x (i) if $y = 3x^2 + x$, (ii) if $xy = x^2 + 1$.

The procedure to be adopted when neither x nor y is an explicit function of the other is illustrated in Example 7.

Example 7. *Find the gradient at the point* (1, 2) *of the ellipse*

$$x^2 - 3xy + 2y^2 - y = 1.$$

[y is an implicit function of x, so we can differentiate term by term, regarding each side of this equation as a function of x.]

Differentiating with respect to x,

$$2x - 3\left(y + x\frac{dy}{dx}\right) + 4y\frac{dy}{dx} - \frac{dy}{dx} = 0.$$

$$\therefore \frac{dy}{dx}(-3x + 4y - 1) = -2x + 3y.$$

$$\therefore \text{ at } (1, 2), \frac{dy}{dx} = \frac{4}{4} = 1.$$

Thus the required gradient is 1.

$\frac{d}{dx}x^n$ for all rational values of n

7·11. (i) *When n is a positive integer.* This has been proved in § 7·3.

(ii) *When n is a positive fraction.* Let $n = \frac{p}{q}$, where p and q are integers.

Let $y = x^n = x^{p/q}$.

$$\therefore y^q = x^p.$$

$$\therefore \frac{d}{dx}y^q = \frac{d}{dx}x^p.$$

$$\therefore \frac{d}{dy}y^q\frac{dy}{dx} = px^{p-1}.*$$

$$\therefore qy^{q-1}\frac{dy}{dx} = px^{p-1}.$$

$$\therefore \frac{dy}{dx} = \frac{p}{q}\frac{x^{p-1}}{y^{q-1}} = \frac{p}{q}\frac{x^{p-1}y}{y^q} = \frac{p}{q}\frac{x^p}{x^p}\frac{y}{x} = \frac{p}{q}\frac{x^{p/q}}{x} = nx^{n-1}.$$

It should be noted that if q is even $x^{p/q}$ has two real values; the same value must be taken throughout.

* This step depends on the differentiation of a function of a function. See note at end of Ex. 8, § 7·6.

(iii) *When n is negative.* Let $n = -p$.

Let
$$y = x^n = x^{-p} = \frac{1}{x^p}.$$

$$\therefore\ yx^p = 1.$$

$$\therefore\ \frac{dy}{dx}x^p + ypx^{p-1} = 0.$$

$$\therefore\ \frac{dy}{dx} = -p\frac{y}{x} = -p\frac{x^n}{x} = -px^{n-1} = nx^{n-1}.$$

Second Derived Function

7·12. If we are considering a function of x, say $y = f(x)$, we have seen that its derivative $\frac{dy}{dx}$ or $\frac{d}{dx}f(x)$ measures the rate of change of the function, or the gradient of its graph.

The rate of change of its gradient is measured by $\frac{d}{dx}\left(\frac{dy}{dx}\right)$, i.e. it is found by differentiating the gradient function.

$\frac{d}{dx}\left(\frac{dy}{dx}\right)$ is generally written $\frac{d^2y}{dx^2}$.

$\frac{d^2y}{dx^2}$ is called the second derivative.

In the same way if $\frac{d^2y}{dx^2}$ is differentiated, for $\frac{d}{dx}\left(\frac{d^2y}{dx^2}\right)$ we write $\frac{d^3y}{dx^3}$, and this is called the third derivative.

Sometimes $\frac{d}{dx}f(x)$ is written as $f'(x)$, and $\frac{d}{dx}f'(x)$ is written as $f''(x)$.

If a particle moving along a straight line is x ft. from the origin at time t sec., we have seen that its velocity at that time is

$$v = \frac{dx}{dt}\text{ ft./sec.}$$

Its acceleration is $\frac{dv}{dt} = \frac{d^2x}{dt^2}$ ft./sec.^{2}.

Parametric Representation

7·13. If $x = f(t)$ and $y = \phi(t)$, $\dfrac{dy}{dx}$ can be found as follows:

$$\frac{dy}{dx} = \lim_{\Delta x \to 0} \frac{\Delta y}{\Delta x} = \lim_{\Delta t \to 0} \left(\frac{\Delta y}{\Delta t} \div \frac{\Delta x}{\Delta t} \right).$$

Hence, assuming the result about the limit of a quotient,

$$\frac{dy}{dx} = \frac{dy}{dt} \div \frac{dx}{dt}, \quad \text{provided} \quad \frac{dx}{dt} \neq 0.$$

Ex. 17. Find $\dfrac{dy}{dx}$ in terms of t

(i) when $x = at^2$, $y = 2at$,

(ii) when $x = \dfrac{2t}{1-t^2}$, $y = \dfrac{1+t^2}{1-t^2}$.

7·14. Example 8. *If $x = t^2$, $y = 2t$, find $\dfrac{d^2y}{dx^2}$ in terms of t.*

$$\frac{dx}{dt} = 2t, \quad \frac{dy}{dt} = 2.$$

$$\therefore \quad \frac{dy}{dx} = \frac{dy}{dt} \div \frac{dx}{dt} = \frac{1}{t}.$$

$$\therefore \quad \frac{d}{dt}\left(\frac{dy}{dx}\right) = \frac{d}{dt}\left(\frac{1}{t}\right) = -\frac{1}{t^2}.$$

$$\therefore \quad \frac{d^2y}{dx^2} = \frac{d}{dx}\left(\frac{dy}{dx}\right) = \frac{d}{dt}\left(\frac{dy}{dx}\right) \div \frac{dx}{dt} = -\frac{1}{t^2} \div 2t = -\frac{1}{2t^3}.$$

Ex. 18. Find $\dfrac{d^2y}{dx^2}$ in terms of t, when

(i) $x = 2t$, $y = \dfrac{1}{t}$, (ii) $x = t^3$, $y = t^2$, (iii) $x = 2t^2$, $y = \dfrac{1}{t}$.

Exercise 7b

Differentiate Nos. 1–27.

1. $x(x-4)^4$.
2. $(3x-1)^2(5-2x)^3$.
3. $x^n(a-x)^n$.
4. $(x+2)\sqrt{x}$.
5. $(3x+2)\sqrt{(2x^2+1)}$.
6. $\sqrt{(1+x)}\sqrt{(1-x)}$.
7. $\dfrac{x}{x+2}$.
8. $\dfrac{4x-3}{3x+4}$.
9. $\dfrac{a+bx}{c-dx}$.
10. $\dfrac{x+1}{\sqrt{x}}$.
11. $\dfrac{\sqrt{(x^2-1)}}{x}$.
12. $\dfrac{\sqrt{(ax^2+b)}}{bx}$.

---

13. $(x-5)^2(x+6)^3$.
14. $\dfrac{(3x-5)^2}{(2x+3)^3}$.
15. $\sqrt{\dfrac{x}{x+2}}$.
16. $\dfrac{\sqrt{(2x-3)}}{x^2}$.
17. $\dfrac{3}{(x-1)(x+2)}$.
18. $\dfrac{3x-1}{x^3+3}$.
19. $\dfrac{\sqrt{(2x^2+3)}}{5x}$.
20. $\sqrt{\{(4+3x^2)(1-6x)\}}$.
21. $\dfrac{1}{x\sqrt{(x^2+1)}}$.
22. $(3x-5)^2(2x+1)^3$.
23. $(3x-1)\sqrt{(5x^2+2)}$.
24. $\sqrt{\{(2x^2-3)(4-x^2)\}}$
25. $\dfrac{5-2x^3}{7-3x^2}$.
26. $\sqrt{\dfrac{2x-1}{x+2}}$.
27. $\dfrac{1}{x^3\sqrt{(1-3x^2)}}$.

In Nos. 28–30, find $\dfrac{d^2y}{dx^2}$ and $\dfrac{d^3y}{dx^3}$.

28. $y = 3x^4 - 2x^2$.
29. $y = x^{10}$.
30. $y = 8x^{\frac{5}{2}}$.

In Nos. 31—33, find $\dfrac{d^2y}{dx^2}$.

31. $y = (x^2+1)^5$.
32. $y = \dfrac{x}{\sqrt{(x^2+1)}}$.
33. $x^2+y^2 = a^2$.

In Nos. 34–37, find $\dfrac{dy}{dx}$ and $\dfrac{d^2y}{dx^2}$ in terms of t.

34. $x = t^2-1,\ y = t^3$.
35. $x = \dfrac{t^2}{1+t},\ y = \dfrac{t}{1+t}$.
36. $x = \dfrac{t}{t^3+1},\ y = \dfrac{t^2}{t^3+1}$.
37. $x = \dfrac{(1-t^2)}{1+t^2},\ y = \dfrac{2t}{1+t^2}$.

38. For Boyle's law, connecting pressure and volume of a gas, $pv =$ a constant, prove that $\dfrac{dp}{dv} = -\dfrac{p}{v}$. Explain the negative sign.

39. For the hyperbola $2x^2+3xy-2y^2 = 12$, find the gradient at $(2, 1)$, and at the other point at which $x = 2$.

40. The position at time t of a projectile referred to horizontal and vertical axes is given by

$$x = 40t, \quad y = 56t-16t^2.$$

Find at what times the projectile is moving (i) horizontally, (ii) at an angle of 45° to the horizontal.

41. If the pressure and volume of a gas are connected by the adiabatic law $pv^\gamma = c$, where γ and c are constants, show that the volumetric elasticity, $-v\dfrac{dp}{dv}$, varies as p.

42. If $x = t^2+3t$ and $y = 2t+t^3$, find $\dfrac{dy}{dx}$ in terms of t and show that, when $\dfrac{dy}{dx} = 1$, x is either 4 or $-\frac{8}{9}$.

Also find $\dfrac{d^2y}{dx^2}$ in terms of t.

43. Find a maximum or minimum value of $\dfrac{\sqrt{x}}{1+x}$, and show which it is.

44. If $\frac{1}{2}kx^2+lx+m = t$, where k, l, m are constants, verify that

$$\frac{d^2x}{dt^2} = -k\left(\frac{dx}{dt}\right)^3.$$

---

45. For the rectangular hyperbola, $x = a\left(t+\dfrac{1}{t}\right)$, $y = a\left(t-\dfrac{1}{t}\right)$, find $\dfrac{dy}{dx}$, and the points where the tangent is parallel to $x = 0$.

Also find $\dfrac{d^2y}{dx^2}$ in terms of t.

46. For the hyperbola $xy+ax+c = 0$ show that $x^2\dfrac{dy}{dx}$ is constant.

47. For what values of x has $x\sqrt{(1-x^2)}$ (i) a maximum, (ii) a minimum value? Sketch the graph of $y = x\sqrt{(1-x^2)}$.

Also sketch, in a dotted line, the remaining part of the graph of

$$y^2 = x^2(1-x^2).$$

48. If $x^2+2xy+3y^2 = 1$, find $\dfrac{dy}{dx}$, and prove that

$$(x+3y)^3\frac{d^2y}{dx^2}+2 = 0.$$

CHAPTER 8

INTEGRATION AS SUMMATION

8·1. In Chapter 5 we have seen how to find the area under a graph by anti-differentiation. In this chapter we shall consider that problem from a different point of view.

To **integrate** means to find a value by the addition of parts or elements.

The process of integration is illustrated by the following treatment of the example we considered in § 5·7.

8·2. *To find the area bounded by the curve* $y = 5 + \frac{1}{10}x^2$, *the x-axis, and the ordinates* $x = 2$ *and* $x = 10$.

In fig. 8·1, we want to find the area UVSR. The area clearly lies between the area on UV up to the zigzag bounded by the continuous line and the area up to the zigzag bounded by the broken line.

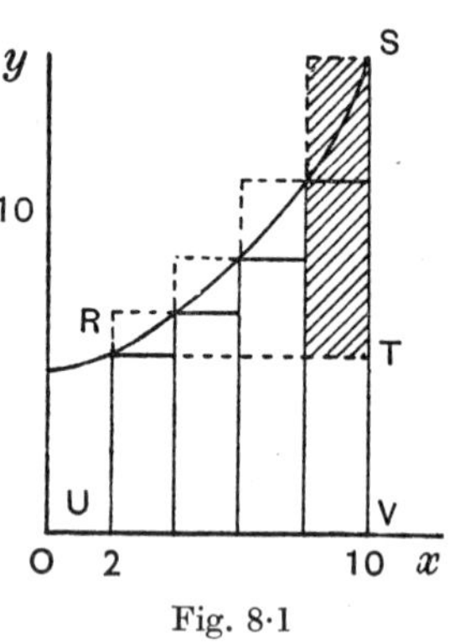

Fig. 8·1

We may say that the required area is shut up between two values. In such a case we naturally ask how close the values are, or what is their difference. We see by geometry that, if the strips are of equal width, this difference is equal to the area shaded in the figure, which is TS × 2.

Obviously it is desirable that this difference should be as small as possible. We cannot alter the length of TS; but, by dividing UV into more and more equal parts, we can make the shaded area narrower and narrower. In that way we can shut up the required area between values that grow closer and closer, or, in other words, whose difference approaches nearer and nearer to zero.

If we divide the required area into 8 strips of equal width as in fig. 8·2, the width of each will be $\frac{10-2}{8} = 1$.

We will call the successive ordinates $y_0, y_1, y_2, \ldots, y_8$.

The area now lies between the values

$$1 \times [y_0+y_1+y_2+\ldots+y_7] = \sum_{r=0}^{r=7} y_r \times 1,$$

and

$$1 \times [y_1+y_2+y_3+\ldots+y_8] = \sum_{r=1}^{r=8} y_r \times 1,$$

where Σ (the Greek capital S, pronounced 'sigma') denotes the sum of all the y's between the limits indicated.

The difference between these values is $(y_8-y_0)\times 1$, i.e. TS $\times$ 1.

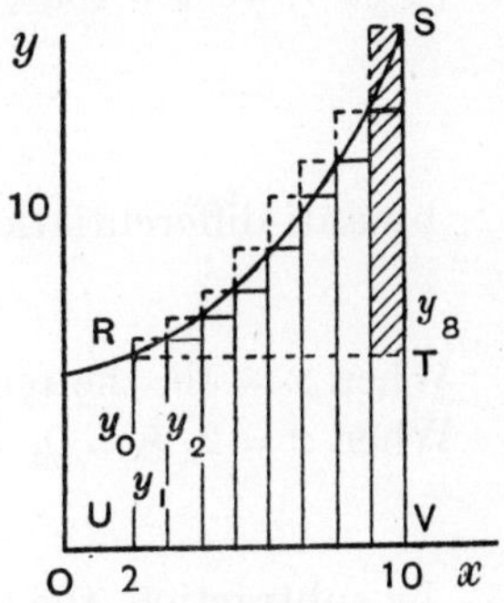

Fig. 8·2

We will now divide the area into n strips

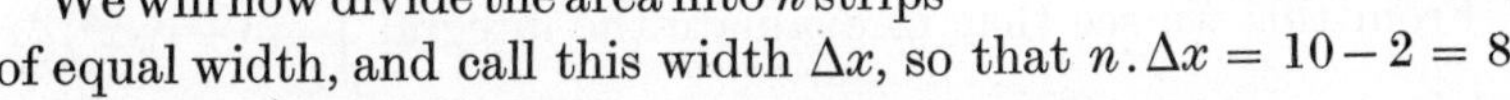

of equal width, and call this width Δx, so that $n.\Delta x = 10-2 = 8$.

We will call the successive ordinates $y_0, y_1, y_2, \ldots, y_n$.

The area now lies between the values

$$(y_0+y_1+y_2+\ldots+y_{n-1})\,\Delta x = \sum_{r=0}^{r=n-1} y_r \Delta x, \tag{i}$$

and

$$(y_1+y_2+y_3+\ldots+y_n)\,\Delta x = \sum_{r=1}^{r=n} y_r \Delta x. \tag{ii}$$

The difference between these values is $(y_n-y_0)\,\Delta x$.

Here y_n-y_0 does not alter whatever n may be; but the larger we make n, the smaller Δx will be, and so the smaller the difference will be. Thus, if (i) approaches a limit, then (ii) approaches the same limit.

From this we may surmise that the area under the graph

$$= \lim_{\Delta x\to 0} \sum_{x=2}^{x=10} y\,\Delta x,$$

the summation being taken from where $x = 2$ to where $x = 10$.

This limit $\lim\limits_{\Delta x\to 0} \sum\limits_{x=2}^{x=10} y\,\Delta x$ is represented by $\int_2^{10} y\,dx$ and is read 'integral $y\,dx$ from $x = 2$ to $x = 10$'.

The sign $\int$ is a degenerate S (for 'sum').

So we see that the area under the curve $y = 5+\frac{1}{10}x^2$ from $x = 2$ to $x = 10$ may be represented by $\int_2^{10} (5+\frac{1}{10}x^2)\,dx$.

8·3. The next step is to see how to evaluate this integral. In § 5·7, we saw that, if A is the area up to (x, y),

$$\frac{dA}{dx} = y = 5 + \tfrac{1}{10}x^2.$$

∴ by anti-differentiation

$$A = 5x + \tfrac{1}{30}x^3 + c.$$

When $x = 10$, the required area $= 50 + \frac{1000}{30} + c$.
When $x = 2$, $A = 0$.

$$\therefore\ 0 = 5 \times 2 + \tfrac{1}{30} \times 2^3 + c.$$

∴ by subtraction, the required area $= (50 + \frac{1000}{30}) - (10 + \frac{8}{30})$.

From this we see that to evaluate the integral $\int_2^{10} (5 + \frac{1}{10}x^2)\,dx$ we anti-differentiate $5 + \frac{1}{10}x^2$ which gives us $5x + \frac{1}{30}x^3 + c$; then we write down the value of this when $x = 10$, and from it take the value when $x = 2$.

This we represent by means of the following notation:

$$\int_2^{10} (5 + \tfrac{1}{10}x^2)\,dx = \Big[5x + \tfrac{1}{30}x^3\Big]_2^{10}$$
$$= (5 \times 10 + \tfrac{1}{30} \times 10^3) - (5 \times 2 + \tfrac{1}{30} \times 2^3)$$
$$= 73\tfrac{1}{15}.$$

Note that it is unnecessary to insert the constant as it would drop out in the subtraction.

8·4. The expression $\int (5 + \frac{1}{10}x^2)\,dx$ is used to denote the result of anti-differentiating $5 + \frac{1}{10}x^2$. It is called an **indefinite integral**, as opposed to $\int_2^{10} (5 + \frac{1}{10}x^2)\,dx$ which is called a **definite integral**; the 2 and the 10 are called the **limits** of the definite integral, and $(5 + \frac{1}{10}x^2)$ is called the **integrand.**

Remember that the easiest way to integrate a term, e.g. x^2 or $(3x + 2)^{\frac{7}{2}}$, is to increase the index by one, and then, by differentiating what has been obtained, to find the appropriate number by which to divide.

Exercise 8*a*.

1. Evaluate the following indefinite integrals:

(i) $\int (x^2+2x+3)\,dx$, (ii) $\int \left(\frac{2}{x^2}-5\right) dx$, (iii) $\int (5x^2-3x+7)\,dx$,

(iv) $\int \sqrt{(x-5)}\,dx$, (v) $\int (3x+2)^2\,dx$, (vi) $\int (7-2x)^{\frac{3}{2}}\,dx$.

2. Evaluate:

(i) $\Big[x^2+3\Big]_0^4$, (ii) $\Big[x^3\Big]_1^2$, (iii) $\Big[2x+3\Big]_{-2}^5$,

(iv) $\left[\frac{x^3}{3}\right]_1^4$, (v) $\left[\frac{x^2}{3}+4x\right]_{-3}^0$, (vi) $\left[\frac{x^4}{4}-\frac{3x^2}{2}\right]_{-2}^2$.

3. Evaluate the following definite integrals:

(i) $\int_0^2 (3x^2-2x)\,dx$, (ii) $\int_1^3 (5x+3)\,dx$, (iii) $\int_{-1}^2 \left(x^2-\frac{1}{x^2}\right) dx$,

(iv) $\int_{-2}^2 \left(6x^2-\frac{1}{x^2}\right) dx$, (v) $\int_{-2}^2 (6x^3-x)\,dx$, (vi) $\int_0^4 2\left(\sqrt{x}+\frac{1}{\sqrt{x}}\right) dx$.

(vii) $\int_0^2 \sqrt{(x+2)}\,dx$, (viii) $\int_4^5 (2x-5)^3\,dx$, (ix) $\int_{-2}^0 (3+2x)\,dx$.

8·5. The example worked out in § 8·3 should be set out as follows:

Example 1. *Find the area bounded by the curve* $y = 5+\frac{1}{10}x^2$, *the* x*-axis and the ordinates* $x = 2$ *and* $x = 10$.

Let the required area be divided up into strips of equal width Δx by ordinates of points on the curve.

If (x, y) and $(x+\Delta x, y+\Delta y)$ are near points on the curve, the element of area $\simeq y\,\Delta x$.*

$\therefore$ Total area from $x = 2$ to $x = 10$

$$= \int_2^{10} y\,dx$$

$$= \int_2^{10} (5+\tfrac{1}{10}x^2)\,dx$$

$$= \left[5x+\tfrac{1}{30}x^3\right]_2^{10}$$

$$= (5\times 10+\tfrac{1}{30}\times 10^3)-(5\times 2+\tfrac{1}{30}\times 2^3)$$

$$= 73\tfrac{1}{15}.$$

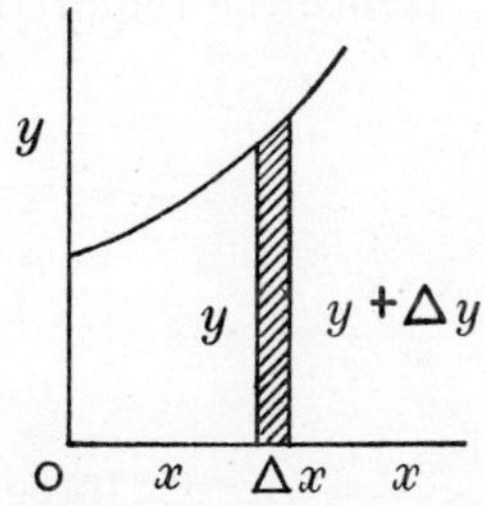

Fig. 8·3

* More strictly the element of area lies between $y\,\Delta x$ and $(y+\Delta y)\,\Delta x$.

8·6. Note the steps in the above example.

(i) Divide the required area into suitable elements.

Note that the elements need not be rectangular. See Ex. 1 below.

(ii) Write down an approximate expression for the typical element.*

(iii) Express the whole area as a definite integral.

(iv) Evaluate this integral.

Ex. 1. Find the area of a circle by dividing it into concentric rings and assuming the expression for the circumference of a circle.

Ex. 2. Make a freehand sketch of the parabola $y^2 = 4ax$. Mark a point P, (h, k), on the curve and draw PM perpendicular to the y-axis. Find the area bounded by OM, MP and the curve, by dividing it into elements by lines parallel to the x-axis, and show that the area is $\frac{1}{3}hk$.

Also, if PN is drawn perpendicular to the x-axis, find the area bounded by ON, NP and the curve, by dividing it into elements by ordinates.

8·7. Example 2. *Find the area enclosed by the curve* $y^2 = 4x$, *the ordinate* $x = 2$ *and the lines* $y = 0$, $y = 2$.

Sketch the curve $y^2 = 4x$ and the line BD, $x = 2$. Insert the line CD, $y = 2$.

The required area is OBDC.

Divide it into elements by lines parallel to the x-axis, as shown in fig. 8·4.

If P is the point (x, y), the length of PQ is $2-x$.

The element of area $\simeq (2-x)\,\Delta y$.†

Hence the required area

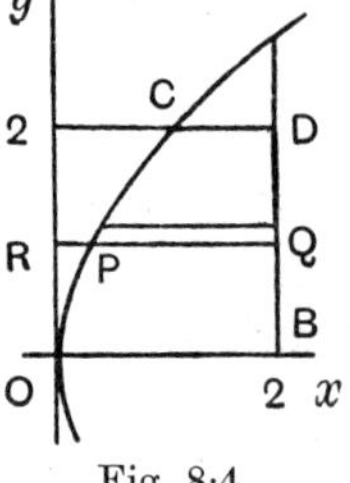

Fig. 8·4

$$= \int_0^2 \left(2 - \frac{y^2}{4}\right) dy$$

$$= \left[2y - \tfrac{1}{12}y^3\right]_0^2$$

$$= 3\tfrac{1}{3}.$$

Integration from First Principles

8·8. We have now met the two main ideas of the calculus. These are differentiation, or the consideration of the limiting value of the ratio of two increments, and integration, or the consideration of the limiting value of the sum of a large number of increments or elements.

* Strictly we consider the typical element as lying between certain bounds.

† More strictly the element of area lies between $(2-x)\,\Delta y$ and $(2-x-\Delta x)\,\Delta y$.

Differentiation 'from first principles' has already been discussed. We have just shown that integration can be carried out by anti-differentiation, but it is interesting to note that integration 'from first principles' is also possible; indeed it was a method known to Archimedes (287–212 B.C.) and his contemporaries before the method of differentiation was discovered. To illustrate the method we shall use it to find the area of a right-angled triangle.

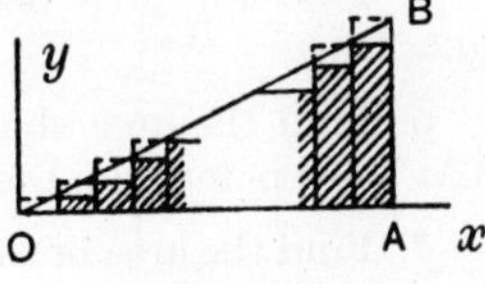

Fig. 8·5

In fig. 8·5 the base of the triangle is OA $= a$ and the height AB $= b$.

Divide OA into n equal parts, each of length h in. On these parts as base (except the first) draw rectangles to fit inside the triangle, as shown.

The height of the first rectangle is $\frac{bh}{a}$, of the second is $\frac{2bh}{a}$, etc. Note that $nh = a$.

The area of the triangle OAB

$$= \lim_{h\to 0}\left[h\left(\frac{bh}{a}\right) + h\left(\frac{2bh}{a}\right) + \ldots + h\left\{\frac{(n-1)\,bh}{a}\right\}\right]$$

$$= \lim_{h\to 0}\frac{bh^2}{a}[1+2+3+\ldots+(n-1)]$$

$$= \lim_{h\to 0}\frac{bh^2}{a}\frac{n(n-1)}{2}$$

$$= \lim_{h\to 0}\frac{b}{2a}hn(hn-h)$$

$$= \lim_{h\to 0}\frac{b}{2a}a(a-h)$$

$$= \tfrac{1}{2}ab.$$

Ex. 3. Find the area of the triangle by considering the sum of the rectangles up to the broken lines in fig. 8·5.

Ex. 4. Use the above method to find the area bounded by the curve $y=x^2$, the x-axis and the ordinate $x=5$.

Use $$\sum_1^n r^2 = \tfrac{1}{6}n(n+1)(2n+1).$$

Exercise 8*b*

Use the method and notation of Examples 1, 2. *In general a sketch of the curve should be made.*

1. Find the area between the curve $y = 3x^2$, the x-axis, and the ordinates $x = 3$, $x = 4$.

2. Find the area between $y = 3x^2+2x$, the x-axis and the line $x = 1$.

3. Find the area between $y = x^2+4$, the line $y = 3$, and the lines $x = 0$, $x = 2$.

4. Find the area cut off between $y = (x-1)(3-x)$ and the x-axis.

5. Find the area between the curve $x = 3y^2$, the y-axis and the line $y = 4$.

6. Find the area shut in by $x = (y-1)^2$, the y-axis and the line $y = 3$. [At what point does the curve touch the y-axis?]

7. Find the area of the segment of the curve $x = y^2-5y+6$ cut off by the y-axis. Why is the result negative?

8. Find the area between the curve $y^2 = 4(x-3)$, the line $x = 1$, and between $y = 1$ and $y = 3$.

9. Find the area bounded by the curve $y = \dfrac{1}{(1-x)^2}$ and the lines $x = 1$, $y = 0$, $y = 4$. [Find the points on the curve at which $x = 0$ and at which $y = 4$.]

---

10. Find the area between the curve $y = 1+2x+6x^2$, the x-axis and the lines $x = 2$, $x = 3$.

11. Find the area bounded by the curve $xy^2 = 10$, the y-axis and the lines $y = 2$, $y = 5$.

12. Find the area intercepted between the curve $y = x^2-2x-3$ and the x-axis.

13. Find the area between the curve $y = x^2+2x-1$ and the line $y = 1$.

14. Find the area between the curve $x = (4-y)(y-1)$ and the y-axis.

15. Find the area between the curve $y = x^2+2$, the y-axis and the line $y = 6$. Also find the area between the curve and the line $y = 6$.

16. Find the area between the curve $x = 5-y^2$, the x-axis and the line $x = 1$.

17. Find the area between the curve $x = 4y-y^2$ and the line $x = 3$.

---

18. Find the area included between the curve $y = 2x^2$ and the line $y = 4x$.

19. P is the point $(2, 4)$ on the curve $y^3 = 4x^4$. Find the area enclosed by the curve and the line OP.

20. Find the area included between the curve $y^2 = 4x$ and the line $x+y = 0$.

21. Find the area between the parabola $x^2 = y$ and the line $y-x = 2$.

---

22. Find the area between the curve $x^2 = 4y$ and the line $x = y$.

23. The line $y = 2x$ cuts the parabola $y = x(4-x)$ at the origin and at a point A. It also cuts the line $x = 4$ at a point B. Find the areas enclosed by (i) the curve and the line OA, (ii) the curve, the line AB and the line $x = 4$.

24. Find the area between the parabola $y^2 = 4x$ and the line $3y-2x = 4$.

25. Find the area between the two curves $y^2 = ax$ and $ax^3 = y^4$.

8·9. The work in § 8·2 assumes that, as x increases, y also increases. If y decreases as x increases, the figure would be as in fig. 8·6, and the area below the graph would still lie between

$\sum_{r=0}^{r=n-1} y_r \Delta x$ (which would be greater than the required area) and $\sum_{r=1}^{r=n} y_r \Delta x$ (which would be less).

$\therefore$ the required area would still be $\int y\,dx$ between the given limits.

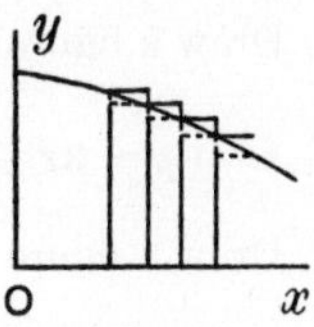

Fig. 8·6

8·10. In the case of a figure such as fig. 8·7, the area can be divided up into parts.

By considering the areas separately, we see that the area from $x=a$ to $x=d$ is

$$\int_a^b y\,dx + \int_b^c y\,dx + \int_c^d y\,dx.$$

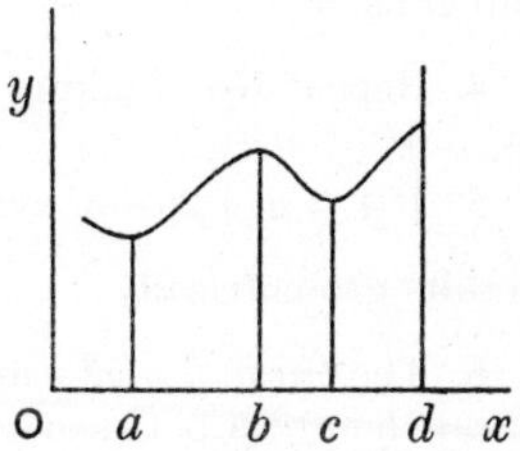

Fig. 8·7

If $\int y\,dx = f(x)$,

$$\begin{aligned} \text{the area} &= \Big[f(x)\Big]_a^b + \Big[f(x)\Big]_b^c + \Big[f(x)\Big]_c^d \\ &= f(b)-f(a)+f(c)-f(b)+f(d)-f(c) \\ &= f(d)-f(a) \\ &= \int_a^d y\,dx. \end{aligned}$$

8·11. If a curve lies below the x-axis, as in fig. 8·8, the values of y are all negative, and therefore the summation which gives the area is the sum of negative terms. Hence the value obtained for the integral will be negative.

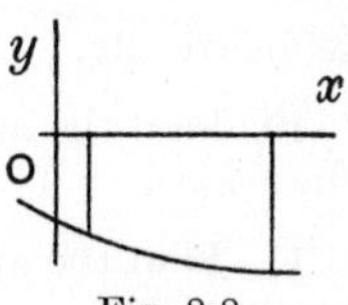

Fig. 8·8

Ex. 5. Find the area bounded by the curve $y = -3x^2$, the x-axis and the ordinates $x = 1$ and $x = 2$.

In evaluating the area in fig. 8·9 from $x=0$ to $x=c$, $\int_0^c y\,dx$ would give 'the area of A – the area of B'.

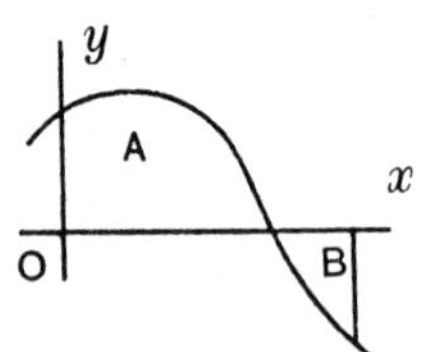

Fig. 8·9

Exercise 8*c*

1. If $y = 5-x$, find (i) $\int_0^5 y\,dx$, (ii) $\int_5^{10} y\,dx$, (iii) $\int_0^{10} y\,dx$. Draw a figure and check your results geometrically.

2. If $y = 3x-12$, find (i) $\int_0^4 y\,dx$, (ii) $\int_4^8 y\,dx$, (iii) $\int_0^8 y\,dx$. Draw a figure and check your results geometrically.

3. Evaluate (i) $\int_0^2 (4+3x-x^2)\,dx$, (ii) $\int_0^2 (3x-x^2)\,dx$. Sketch the curves and indicate what areas are given by the two definite integrals.

4. Repeat No. 3 taking the integrals from 0 to 4.

5. If $x = y^2+2y-3$, evaluate (i) $\int_{-3}^0 x\,dy$, (ii) $\int_{-3}^1 x\,dy$. Interpret your results geometrically.

6. The curve $y = x^3-6x^2+11x-6$ cuts the x-axis at $x = 1$, $x = 2$, $x = 3$. Find the areas between the curve and the x-axis (i) from $x = 1$ to $x = 2$, (ii) from $x = 2$ to $x = 3$. Explain why your answers have different signs.

---

7. Evaluate (i) $\int_0^2 (x^2-4x)\,dx$, (ii) $\int_0^4 (x^2-4x)\,dx$, (iii) $\int_0^6 (x^2-4x)\,dx$. Interpret your results geometrically.

8. Find the areas of the segments of the curve $y = x(x-2)(x-3)$ cut off by the x-axis.

9. Evaluate (i) $\int_0^2 (2-y)^3\,dy$, (ii) $\int_0^4 (2-y)^3\,dy$, and interpret the results geometrically.

10. Find the areas of the segments of the curve $y = x(x^2-4)$ cut off by the x-axis.

11. Find the area of the segment of the curve $y = (x+1)^2(x-2)$ cut off by the x-axis.

8·12. In the following example we use the idea of summation to find the volume of a solid of revolution.

Example 3. *A circular bowl has a vertical central section in the shape of a curve whose equation is* $y = ax^2$. *The diameter of the top of the bowl is* 12 *in. and its depth is* 2 *in. How much water will the bowl hold?*

Fig. 8·10 shows the central section.

The point (6, 2) is on the curve,

$$\therefore\ 2 = a \times 6^2,$$

$$\therefore\ a = \tfrac{1}{18},$$

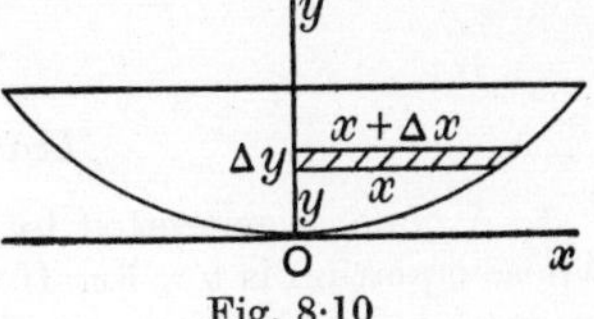

Fig. 8·10

and the equation of the curve is $y = \frac{1}{18}x^2$.

Let (x, y) and $(x+\Delta x, y+\Delta y)$ be near points on the curve.

Divide the required volume into elements by horizontal planes.

The element of volume is obtained by rotating the shaded area about the y-axis. It is approximately a circular disk, and its volume $\simeq \pi x^2 \Delta y$.

$$\therefore \text{ the total volume } = \int_0^2 \pi x^2 dy$$

$$= \int_0^2 \pi 18 y\, dy$$

$$= \Big[\pi . 9y^2\Big]_0^2$$

$$= 9\pi(2^2 - 0^2)$$

$$= 36\pi.$$

$\therefore$ the bowl will hold 36π cu.in. of water.

Ex. 6. Find the volume of a right pyramid of height h on a square base whose side is a. [Divide it into elements by planes parallel to the base.]

Ex. 7. Find the volume of a sphere by dividing it into elements by planes perpendicular to a diameter.

Ex. 8. Find the volume of a sphere of radius r by dividing it into elements by concentric spherical surfaces and assuming the area of a sphere to be $4\pi r^2$.

Also find the volume by considering the volume of a pyramid with its vertex at the centre and whose base is a small element of the surface of the sphere.

¶Ex. 9. $y^2 = 4ax$ represents a parabola whose axis of symmetry is the x-axis. By rotating the curve about the x-axis, a paraboloid of revolution is formed. Of what form are sections of this surface made by planes perpendicular to the x-axis? Of what form are sections made by planes containing the x-axis? Find the volume bounded by the paraboloid and the plane perpendicular to the x-axis at $x = b$. Prove that this is half the circumscribing cylinder.

Exercise 8*d*

Leave π in your answers

1. A cone is generated by revolving about the y-axis the straight line whose equation is $y = 3x$. If the height of the cone is 6 in., find its volume by integration.

2. Find the volume enclosed when the portion of the curve $x = \sqrt{(1-y^2)}$ between $y = \frac{1}{2}$ and $y = 1$ is rotated about the y-axis.

3. The area bounded by the curve $y = x^2(1-x)$ and the lines $x = -1$ and $x = 1$ is rotated about the x-axis. Find the volume enclosed by the resulting surface of revolution.

4. A vessel for holding flowers is of the shape formed by the revolution of the curve $y = 4\sqrt{x}$ about the y-axis; its height is 8 in. How much water will it hold?

5. Find the volume of the solid formed by the revolution about the x-axis of the curve $y^2 = x(a-x)$.

6. A flower bowl is part of a sphere of radius 6 in., and the depth of the bowl is 9 in. How much water will the bowl hold?

7. An equilateral triangle of side $2a$ is rotated (i) about one of its sides, (ii) about a line through a vertex parallel to the opposite side. Find, by integration, the volumes of the solids so formed.

8. The heap of stones shown in fig. 8·11 has a length a ft. and its height is h ft. The sloping faces each make 45° with the horizontal. Show that the area of a horizontal section x ft. below the ridge is $2x(a-2h+2x)$ sq.ft. Hence, by integration, find the volume of the whole heap.

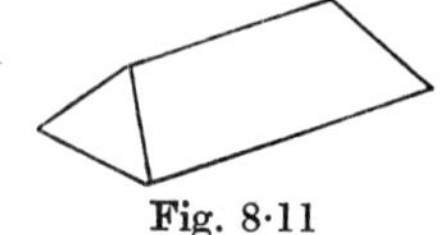

Fig. 8·11

9. The area bounded by the parabola $y^2 = 4x$ and the line $x = 1$ is rotated about the line $x = 1$. Find the volume of the spindle-shaped solid so formed.

10. The area described in No. 9 is rotated about the y-axis. Find the volume of the solid so formed.

¶ For discussion.

11. The inner surface of a saucer is 12 cm. across and 1·5 cm. deep. A section through the axis has the form $y^4 = ax$. Find the value of a and make a sketch of the section. How many c.c. of tea will the saucer hold?

12. A sphere of radius a is divided into two portions by a plane at a distance $a/2$ from the centre. Show that the volume of the smaller portion is $\frac{5}{32}$ of the volume of the sphere.

13. The curve $y = x^{\frac{1}{2}}$ is rotated about the x-axis. Find the volume enclosed by the surface of revolution between the sections $x = 4$ and $x = 9$.

Also find the volume enclosed when the same portion of the curve is rotated about the y-axis.

14. The area bounded by the rectangular hyperbola $xy = 1$, the x-axis, and the ordinates $x = 1$ and $x = 2$, is rotated about the y-axis. Find the volume of the ring-shaped solid so formed.

15. The part of the curve $y = \sqrt{(20x-x^2)}$ between $x = 0$ and $x = 10$ is a quarter of a circle. The arc of the curve from $x = 0$ to $x = a$ is revolved about the x-axis. If the volume of the bowl obtained is one-half that of the bowl obtained by revolving the whole quadrant, show that $30a^2 - a^3 = 1000$.

Find two integers between which a lies.

16. Sketch the curve $2y^2 = x(1-x)^2$, and find the volume of the solid obtained by rotating the loop about the x-axis.

17. The area enclosed by the curves $y = x^2$ and $x = y^2$ is rotated about the x-axis. Find the volume of the solid of revolution.

18. A hole of radius 3 in. is bored right through a solid sphere of radius 5 in. so that the axis of the hole is a diameter of the sphere. Find the volume of the remaining part of the sphere, and prove that it is equal to the volume of a sphere of radius 4 in.

19. The area cut off from the parabola $y^2 = 8x$ by the chord $x = 2$ is revolved about the line $x = 5$. Find the volume of the solid so formed.

Mean Values

8·13. If a quantity y takes a set of n different values

$$y_1, y_2, y_3, \ldots, y_n,$$

the expression

$$\frac{y_1+y_2+y_3+\ldots+y_n}{n}$$

is called the average value of y. It is also called the **arithmetic mean** of the values of y, or the **mean value** of y.

If y is given as a function of $x, f(x)$, and a table is made showing the values of y for equal increments of x, we can draw the curve $y = f(x)$.

In fig. 8·12, the curve is the graph of $y = f(x)$. We want to find the mean value of y for equal increments of x from $x = a$ to $x = b$.

If $y_1, y_2, y_3, \ldots$, are the ordinates drawn at equal intervals Δx from $x = a$ to $x = b$

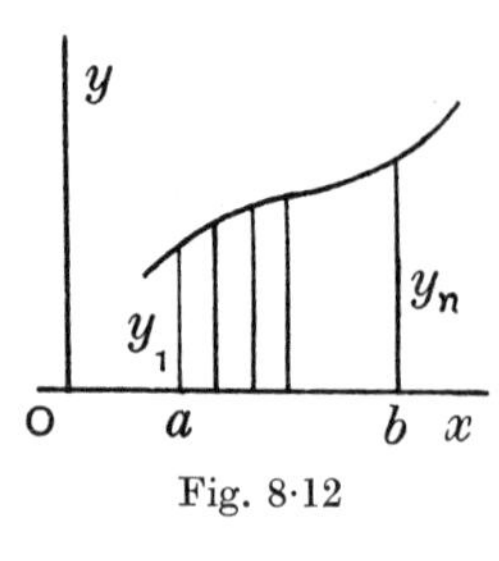

Fig. 8·12

$$\lim_{n\to\infty} \frac{y_1+y_2+y_3+\ldots+y_n}{n} = \lim_{n\to\infty} \frac{\Sigma y}{n}$$

$$= \lim_{n\to\infty} \frac{\Sigma y\,\Delta x}{n\,\Delta x}$$

$$= \frac{1}{b-a}\int_a^b y\,dx,$$

since $n\,\Delta x = b-a$.

So we have the following definition:

When y is a known function of x, the **mean value** of y for equal changes in the value of x from $x = a$ to $x = b$ is defined to be

$$\frac{1}{b-a}\int_a^b y\,dx.$$

8·14. This idea of the mean value of a continuously varying quantity is required in science, for example, in the electrical theory of alternating currents, where the square root of the mean value of the square of the current is known as the equivalent constant current (or the **virtual** current).

Ex. 10. Find the mean value of the ordinates of the parabola $y = x^2+2$ between $x = 0$ and $x = 3$.

Ex. 11. Find the mean value of the ordinates of the parabola $y^2 = x+2$ between $x = 2$ and $x = 7$.

Ex. 12. Find the mean value of the velocity (v) of a particle for the first 4 sec. of its motion if $v = 8-3t$.

8·15. When finding the mean value of a function which may be considered to be dependent upon different variables, it is important to discover which variable is meant. This is illustrated in the following example.

Example 4. *A particle is projected vertically upwards with velocity 96 ft./sec. Find the mean value of the velocity during the upward flight*

(i) *considered as a function of the time,*

(ii) *considered as a function of the distance.*

(*Take g as 32 ft./sec.*^{2})

(i) t sec. after the start the velocity is given by $v = 96 - 32t$, and the particle ascends for 3 sec.

The mean value of the velocity is then

$$\frac{1}{3}\int_0^3 v\,dt = \frac{1}{3}\Big[961 - 16t^2\Big]_0^3$$
$$= 48.$$

$\therefore$ the mean value of the velocity considered as a function of the time is 48 ft./sec.

(ii) Suppose the height of the particle t sec. after the start is x ft.

Then $v^2 = (96)^2 - 64x$, and the particle ascends 144 ft.

The mean value of the velocity is then

$$\frac{1}{144}\int_0^{144} v\,dx = \frac{1}{144}\int_0^{144} \sqrt{\{(96)^2 - 64x\}}\,dx$$
$$= \frac{1}{144}\left[-\frac{1}{64}\cdot\frac{2}{3}\{(96)^2 - 64x\}^{\frac{3}{2}}\right]_0^{144}$$
$$= 64.$$

$\therefore$ the mean value of the velocity considered as a function of the distance is 64 ft./sec.

Note that the mean value found in (i) is the one usually referred to as the 'average velocity'.

Exercise 8*e*

1. Find the mean values from 0 to 2 of (i) x, (ii) x^2, (iii) x^3.

2. Find the mean value of y, where $y = 3 + 4x + 6x^2$, as x changes from -2 to $+2$.

3. When a stone falls from rest the distance s ft. fallen in t sec. is given approximately by $s = 16t^2$. A stone is dropped from a height of 256 ft. Find the mean value of its velocity while it is falling (i) for equal intervals of time (ii) for equal increases in the distance fallen.

4. If a hemisphere of radius a is cut by equidistant planes parallel to its plane face, find the mean value of the sectional areas.

Note that the result $= \dfrac{\text{volume}}{\text{radius}}$.

5. Find the mean value of the cross-sectional area of a right circular cone of height h and base radius a by planes parallel to the base at equal distances along its axis.

Note that the result $= \dfrac{\text{volume}}{\text{height}}$.

6. A volume (v c.c.) of gas under a pressure of p gm. wt./sq.cm. expands in accordance with the law $pv^{1\cdot 2} = 600$. Calculate the mean value of the pressure when the volume changes from 32 to 243 c.c.

---

7. A hopper used for filling a furnace is in the form of a frustum of a pyramid. The top is a square of side a, the bottom a square of side b, and the height is h. Find the mean value of the areas of equidistant sections parallel to the top face.

8. A sphere of radius 2 ft. begins to expand so that its radius increases uniformly at the rate of 1 in./sec. Find, in cubic feet, the mean value of the volume

(i) for equal intervals of time, for the first 12 sec.,
(ii) for equal increases in the radius from 2 to 3 ft.

9. A particle is projected vertically upwards with velocity u ft./sec. Call the retardation g ft./sec.² Find the mean value of its velocity

(i) for equal intervals of time, during the first t sec.,
(ii) for equal increases of distance travelled, up to the greatest height.

10. A particle moves in a straight line so that it is x ft. from a fixed point on the line t sec. after passing O. Its velocity v ft./sec. is given by $v = 3t^2 + 2$. Find the mean value of its distance from O for the first 5 sec. of its motion (i) when x is considered as a function of t, (ii) when x is considered as a function of v.

11. If the parabola $y = a + bx + cx^2$ passes through the points $(-h, y_1)$, $(0, y_2)$, (h, y_3), find a, b, c in terms of h, y_1, y_2, y_3.

Find the mean value of y as x changes from $-h$ to $+h$.

ANSWERS

CHAPTER 1

PAGE

1.2. **Ex. 4.** (i) $0{\cdot}41\pi$ sq.in., (ii) $(4h+h^2)\,\pi$ sq.in.

Ex. 5. 400 ft.; 84 ft.; $(160h+16h^2)$ ft.

Ex. 6. (i) -5, (ii) $-2\frac{1}{4}$, (iii) $-4h-h^2$.

CHAPTER 2

1.5. **Ex. 1.** (i) 6, (ii), 4, (iii) -2.

1.8. **Ex. 2.** 2, 6, 8.

Exercise 2*a*

1.10. 1. $4x$. Twice the gradient of $y=x^2$. 2. $10x$. Five times that of $y=x^2$.
3. x. Half that of $y=x^2$. 4. $2ax$. 5. $2x$, $2x$, $2ax$.

Exercise 2*b*

1.12. 1. (i) $2x$, (ii) $2x+3$, (iii) $6x+1$, (iv) $\frac{1}{2}-\frac{3}{2}x$, (v) $-\frac{8}{3}x+4$, (vi) $2ax+b$.
2. See § 5·2. 3. $3-2x$. 4. $4\frac{1}{3}$, $-\frac{1}{3}$.
6. (8, 7). 7. $-\frac{2}{3}$, $\frac{2}{3}$.

Exercise 2*c*

1.14. 1. (i) (1, 5), max. (ii) (2, -9), min. (iii) (2, -1), min.
2. (i) 5, 5, (ii) 5, 5. 3. A square.
4. $(6x-\frac{1}{2}x^2)$ sq.in.; when $x=6$. 5. 1, 16 ft.
6. $\frac{11}{12}$. 7. After 3 hr.; 5 miles.
8. (i) (2, 10), max. (ii) $(1\frac{1}{2}, 4\frac{1}{2})$, max. (iii) ($-2$, 2), min.

1.15. 9. $4\frac{1}{2}$. 10. $2(x^2-4x+8)$ sq.in.; $2\sqrt{2}$ in.
11. 1. 12. 5. 13. 9 sq.in.
14. $\frac{1}{1728}(l^3-3l^2x+3lx^2)$; $2\left(\frac{l}{24}\right)^3=\frac{l^3}{6912}$. 15. 6 in., 6 in.

Exercise 2*d*

1.16. 1. 8π sq.cm. 2. $1{\cdot}6\times10^{-5}$ ft. 3. 150 ft.; 5 ft.

1.17. 4. 2·1 cu.in.; 1 %.

CHAPTER 3

1.18. **Ex. 1.** 16, 36, 64, 144, 256 ft.
(i) 80 ft./sec., (ii) 64 ft./sec., (iii) 48 ft./sec., (iv) 40 ft./sec.

Ex. 2. $(32+16h)$ ft./sec.

Exercise 3*a*

PAGE

1.19. **1.** (i) 230 yd./min. (ii) 770 yd./min. (iii) 500 yd./min.; 500 yd./min.

1.20. **2.** 5·7, 8·3 degrees/sec. **3.** 2·2, 1·8, 1·2 degrees/min.

4. 1·3, 0·5 gal./sec.

5.

Time in sec.	0	10	20	30	35	40	50
Velocity in yd./sec.	0	6·5	13	27	37	27	0

Exercise 3*b*

1. (i) 4, 2, 2, 4, 8 ft. from the end. (ii) -3, -1, 1, 3, 5 ft./sec.
(iii) At $1\frac{1}{2}$ sec. (iv) $1\frac{3}{4}$ ft. from the end.
(v) +ve after $1\frac{1}{2}$ sec.; −ve before $1\frac{1}{2}$ sec. (vi) Least.

1.21. **2.** (i) 5, -3, -7, -7, -3 ft. from the end.
(ii) -10, -6, -2, 2, 6 ft./sec.
(iii) At $2\frac{1}{2}$ sec.
(iv) $7\frac{1}{2}$ ft. from the end in the negative direction.
(v) +ve after $2\frac{1}{2}$ sec.; −ve before $2\frac{1}{2}$ sec.
(vi) Least (i.e. greatest in negative direction).

3. $(2t-12)$ ft./sec.; after 6 sec.

4. (i) $2\frac{1}{2}v$ ft./sec., (ii) $1\frac{2}{3}v$ ft./sec.

Exercise 3*c*

1.22. **1.** 0·74 ft./sec.^{2} **2.** (i) -26 ft./sec.^{2}, (ii) -22 ft./sec.^{2}

3. (i) $1\frac{1}{2}$ ft., (ii) $(-2+t)$ ft./sec. (iv) -2 ft./sec.,
(v) After 2 sec. (vi) After 1 and 3 sec.
(vii) 1 ft./sec.^{2} in each case.

4. -1 ft./sec.; 0; 2 ft./sec.^{2}

5. (i) 4 ft./sec. (ii) -6 ft./sec.^{2} (iii) 6 ft./sec.^{2} (iv) 3 ft./sec.^{2}

6. 36 ft./sec.; -28 ft./sec.; -32 ft./sec.^{2}

Exercise 3*d*

1.24. **1.** $2{\cdot}4\pi$ $(=7{\cdot}54)$ sq.in./sec. **2.** $48\pi a$, $72\pi a$ sq.in./sec.

3. $\dfrac{b}{2\pi ax}$ in./sec. **4.** Where $x=2$; where $x=1{\cdot}5$.

5. $y=\dfrac{3x}{4}-\dfrac{x^2}{400}$; 80, $60-32t$, $\dfrac{3}{4}-\dfrac{x}{200}$; 80, -4, $-\frac{1}{20}$; 160, 56;
$D_t y=0$ when $t=\frac{15}{8}$; 150.

6. $y=\dfrac{6x}{5}-\dfrac{x^2}{25}$; 20, $24-32t$, $\dfrac{6}{5}-\dfrac{2x}{25}$; 20, -40, -2; 40, -16;
$D_t y=0$ when $t=\frac{3}{4}$; 9.

7. 2·3, 1·4 in./min.; $2\frac{7}{9}$, $\frac{5}{12}\sqrt{10}$ $(=1{\cdot}32)$ in./min.

8. $50-\dfrac{4x}{125}$; at $1562\frac{1}{2}$ ft.

Exercise 4*a*

PAGE

1.25. 1. 14, 23, 7, 167. 2. 2, 1, 5, 2·5. 3. $4x^2+7x+3$.

4. $-x^3+3x^2-7x+1$. 5. $2x^2+3x$; 0, $-\frac{3}{2}$. 6. x^3-8; 2.

7. $x^2+x(2h+3)+h^2+3h+4$.

Exercise 4*b*

1.26. 1. 23; $3a^2+11$; $3x^2+6x\Delta x+3(\Delta x)^2+11$.

2. $2t^2-7t+5+\Delta t(4t-7)+2(\Delta t)^2$.

3. $3\Delta x(x^2+1)+3x(\Delta x)^2+(\Delta x)^3$. 4. $-\dfrac{\Delta x}{x(x+\Delta x)}$.

Exercise 4*c*

1.28. 2. 12. 3. (i) $\frac{3}{4}$, (ii) 27.

1.29. 4. $x=\pm\sqrt{\frac{1}{3}}=\pm 0{\cdot}577$. 6. $x=\pm 1$. 7. 0; $(-3, 28)$.

8. 9. 9. 12; (4, 11).

10. -1, 3 at each point. 12. 11, $-\frac{1}{3}$. 13. $OQ=\frac{2}{3}x$.

14. $-\dfrac{100}{x^2}$.

1.30. 15. $a=1$, $b=-2$, $c=1$.

Exercise 4*d*

1.32 1. $x^2-4x+\dfrac{3}{x^2}$.

2. (i) $-2x^2-\dfrac{1}{2x^2}-x$, (ii) $\dfrac{3}{5x^2}+\dfrac{x^2}{2}$,

(iii) $3+12x^2-12x+\dfrac{3}{x^2}$, (iv) $6x-4-\dfrac{7}{x^2}$.

3. (i) $6+6x^2$, (ii) $-\dfrac{3}{x^2}+5+12x$,

(iii) $4+24x+27x^2$, (iv) $12x^2+\dfrac{3}{x^2}-4x$.

1.33. 4. $-\frac{1}{4}$. 5. $2a-6b\theta^2$.

6. (i) $x>5$ or <1 positive; $5>x>1$ negative.
(ii) $x>3$ or $2>x>1$ positive; $3>x>2$ or $x<1$ negative.
(iii) $4>x>2$ positive; $x>4$ or $x<2$ negative.
(iv) $5>x>-3$ positive; $x>5$ or $x<-3$ negative.
(v) $x<3$ positive; $x>3$ negative.
(vi) $x>2$ or $1>x>-1$ or $x<-2$ positive;
$2>x>1$ or $-1>x>-2$ negative.

8. (i) Min. $(1, -2)$, max. $(-1, 2)$. (ii) Min. $(3, 0)$, max. $(1, \frac{4}{3})$.
(iii) Min. $(\frac{1}{2}, 4)$, max. $(-\frac{1}{2}, -4)$. (iv) Min. $(1, -4)$, max. $(-1, 0)$.
(v) Min. $(1, 1\frac{1}{2})$. (vi) Min. $(\frac{1}{2}\sqrt{2}, \frac{3}{4}\sqrt{2})$, max. $(-\frac{1}{2}\sqrt{2}, -\frac{3}{4}\sqrt{2})$.

9. $24+6x-3x^2$.

10. When number $=1$; when number $=-1$. 11. $1-\dfrac{4}{x^2}$.

PAGE

1.33. 12. (i) Min. $(1, -5)$, max. $(3, -1)$.
(ii) Min. $(2, 0)$, max. $(\frac{4}{3}, \frac{4}{27})$.
(iii) Min. $(2, 5)$, max. $(\frac{2}{3}, 6\frac{5}{27})$.
(iv) Min. $(\sqrt{3}, -6\sqrt{3})$, max. $(-\sqrt{3}, 6\sqrt{3})$.
(v) Max. $(2, 36)$, min. $(\frac{20}{3}, -\frac{400}{27})$.
(vi) Min. $(2, -9\frac{1}{3})$, max. $(1, -8\frac{2}{3})$, min. $(-1, 8\frac{2}{3})$, max. $(-2, 9\frac{1}{3})$.

13. 2.

14. $8x - \dfrac{27}{x^2}$; $x = \frac{3}{2}$, min.

Exercise 4*e*

1.34. 1. $2\left(x + \dfrac{100}{x}\right)$ sq.in.; when $x = 10$ (the rectangle is then a square).

2. $(14 - 2x)$ ft.; $x^2(14 - 2x)$ cu.ft.; 4·7; 102 cu.ft.

3. $x = \frac{2}{3}$.

4. $x(a - 2x)(\frac{1}{2}b - x)$; $3 - \sqrt{3}$ $(= 1{\cdot}27)$ in.; $12\sqrt{3} = 20{\cdot}8$ cu.in.

5. $\sqrt[3]{80}$, $\sqrt[3]{80}$ $(= 4{\cdot}31)$, $\frac{1}{2}\sqrt[3]{80}$ $(= 2{\cdot}15)$ in.

7. $3\pi^{\frac{1}{3}} \times 10^{\frac{14}{3}} = 204{,}000$.

1.35. 8. $\dfrac{1000}{9\pi}\sqrt{3\pi} = 108{\cdot}6$ cu.in.

10. 4 in.

11. When height $= 2\sqrt{\frac{1}{3}} \times$ radius of sphere.

12. $\frac{1}{3}\pi h^2(2\mathrm{R} - h)$.

13. $\left(2a^2 + 3cx + \dfrac{4a^2c}{x}\right)$ sq.in.; 4:3.

14. (i) 2 ft., 2 cu.ft.; (ii) 2 ft., $\dfrac{8}{\pi} = 2{\cdot}55$ cu.ft.

Exercise 4*f*

1. (i) $59\frac{7}{27}$ ft., (ii) $29\frac{17}{27}$ ft.; $\frac{10}{396}$.

1.36. 2. Side of base $\frac{1}{2}a\sqrt[3]{4}$ ft., height $a\sqrt[3]{4}$ ft.

3. Breadth $\frac{1}{2}$ ft., depth 1 ft.

4. $\sqrt{2}:1$.

5. £$\left(\dfrac{1750}{v} + 2v^2\right)c$; 7·6.

6. £$\left(\dfrac{x^2}{72} + \dfrac{180}{x}\right)$; 18·6 mi./hr.; £14. 10*s*.

7. $a = \frac{1}{2}$, $b = 1800$; 60 mi./hr.; £60.

8. 9·2 knots.

1.37. 9. $\sqrt{\dfrac{b}{a}}$.

Exercise 4*g*

1. (i) 229 ft., (ii) 149 ft./sec.; (iii) 72 ft./sec.^{2}

2. (i) 41 ft., (ii) 5 ft./sec., (iii) -10 ft./sec.^{2}

3. 28 ft./sec.; 26 ft./sec.^{2}.

4. 42, 67 ft./sec., 22, 28 ft./sec.^{2}; 54 ft.

PAGE

1.37. 5. (i) 10 ft. from O, (ii) $(8-6t+t^2)$ ft./sec., (iii) $t=2$, $t=4$, (iv) -2, 2 ft./sec.^{2}

7. (i) 26 ft./sec., (ii) 26·5 ft./sec., (iii) 25·75 ft./sec.

1.38. 8. (i) 63 ft./sec., (ii) 62·75 ft./sec., (iii) 27 ft./sec.^{2}

9. (i) $(b+6c+28d)$ ft./sec., (ii) $(b+6c+27d)$ ft./sec., (iii) $(2c+18d)$ ft./sec.^{2}

10. (i) $(96+24h+2h^2)$ ft./sec., (ii) $(96-24h+2h^2)$ ft./sec., (iii) $(96+2h^2)$ ft./sec.

Exercise 4*h*

1. $3x^2$; 130 cu.in.; 132·867 cu.in.
2. $\frac{1}{36}$ in./sec., $\frac{1}{3}$ sq.in./sec.
3. 40π $(=125{\cdot}7)$ cu.cm.
4. $8\pi = 25{\cdot}1$ cu.in./min.
5. (i) $\dfrac{1}{36\pi} = 0{\cdot}00885$ in./sec. (ii) $\dfrac{1}{400\pi} = 0{\cdot}000796$ in./sec., (i) $\frac{2}{3}$ sq.in./sec., (ii) $\frac{2}{10}$ sq.in./sec.

1.39. 6. $\frac{12}{100}x^3$ cu.ft.; $\frac{1000}{576} = 1{\cdot}74$ ft./min.

7. $y=\pi(24x-x^2)$; $\pi(24-2x)$ sq.in./sec.; $12\pi = 37{\cdot}7$ sq.in./sec.

8. $\frac{1}{3}\pi x^3$ cu.ft.; $\dfrac{1}{2\pi} = 0{\cdot}159$ ft./min.

9. $\frac{1}{24}$ in./sec.

10. $V=\pi x^2(12+\frac{2}{3}x)$.

11. $\frac{1}{5}\pi = 0{\cdot}628$ cu.in.

12. $\frac{116}{3}\pi = 121{\cdot}5$ cu.ft./sec.

13. 2 % per sec.

Exercise 5*a*

1.41. 1. $y=x^2+c$. 2. $y=\frac{1}{2}x^2+c$. 3. $y=\frac{1}{2}ax^2+c$. 4. $y=\frac{1}{3}x^3+c$.

5. $y=\frac{1}{3}ax^3+c$. 6. $y=\frac{1}{3}px^3+\frac{1}{2}qx^2+rx+c$.

7. $y=\dfrac{1}{x}+c$. 8. $y=-\dfrac{2}{t}+c$. 9. $y=-\dfrac{a}{t}+bt+\frac{1}{2}ct^2+k$.

Exercise 5*b*

1.42. 1. (i) $\frac{4}{3}x^3-\frac{5}{2}x^2+x+c$. (ii) $x^2-x+\dfrac{5}{x}+c$. (iii) $\frac{7}{3}x^3+4x-\dfrac{2}{x}+c$.

(iv) $\frac{1}{9}x^3+\frac{1}{4}x^2+\dfrac{1}{3x}+c$. (v) $\frac{1}{3}x^3-\frac{3}{2}x^2+2x+c$. (vi) $\frac{2}{3}x^3-3x-\dfrac{4}{x}+c$.

(vii) $x+\dfrac{1}{x}+c$. (viii) $\frac{1}{3}x^3-x+\dfrac{12}{x}+c$. (ix) $\frac{1}{3}x^3-3x-\dfrac{4}{x}+c$.

2. $y=x^3-4x^2+4x+5$. 3. $2\frac{2}{3}$. 4. $y=x+\dfrac{4}{x}-4$.

5. Where $x=-1, 1, 2$.

Exercise 5*c*

1.43. 1. x^2+c. 2. $\frac{1}{3}x^3+c$. 3. $3x+c$.

4. $-\dfrac{1}{x}+c$. 5. $\frac{1}{2}ax^2+c$. 6. $-\dfrac{5}{x}+c$.

PAGE

1.43. 7. $\frac{1}{3}pt^3+\frac{1}{2}qt^2+rt+c$. 8. $\frac{5}{3}t^3+\frac{6}{t}+c$. 9. $\frac{1}{3}x^3+\frac{1}{2}x^2-6x+c$.

10. $x+\frac{4}{x}+c$. 11. $t^3-5t-\frac{1}{t}+c$. 12. $\frac{1}{3}x^3-3x+\frac{10}{x}+c$.

Exercise 5*d*

1.44. 1. $s=3+2t+\frac{3}{2}t^2$. 2. $s=\frac{1}{3}t^3+2t^2-5t+\frac{20}{3}$.

3. $s=2t+\frac{1}{t}$ 4. -6 ft. from O; -250 ft.

5. $s=\frac{1}{3}t^3-\frac{1}{t}+\frac{11}{6}$. 6. $s=\frac{1}{3}t^3-2t^2+3t+5$.

7. $s=t+\frac{1}{t}+4$. 8. 22 ft./sec.^{2}; 54 ft.

9. (i) 2 min.; (ii) $\frac{1}{2}$ mi./min. = 30 mi./hr., (iii) $\frac{2}{3}$ mi.

10. (i) 3 min., (ii) $\frac{9}{16}$ mi./min. = $33\frac{3}{4}$ mi./hr., (iii) $1\frac{1}{8}$ mi.

Exercise 5*e*

1.45. 1. $(100+32t)$ ft./sec.; $(100t+16t^2)$ ft.

2. $(100-32t)$ ft./sec.; $(100t-16t^2)$ ft.

3. $112\frac{1}{2}$ ft. 4. 22 ft.

5. When $t=\frac{2}{3}$, min. $=9{\cdot}685$; when $t=-1$, max. $=12$.

6. $10\frac{1}{2}$ ft./sec.; $13\frac{1}{6}$ ft. 7. 250 units of length.

8. $33\frac{5}{6}$ ft.

1.46. 9. 13 ft. from the origin.

Exercise 5*f*

1.47. 1. (i) 16, (ii) 184. 2. $3\frac{3}{4}$. 3. $2a^2$.

4. (i) $2\frac{2}{3}$, (ii) $-\frac{5}{12}$; No. 5. $4\frac{1}{2}$. 6. $-10\frac{2}{3}$.

7. $\frac{1}{6}$. 8. $\frac{9}{16}$. 9. $40\frac{1}{2}$.

1.48. 10. $\frac{1}{12}$. 11. $\frac{1}{a}-\frac{1}{b}$. 12. $49{\cdot}44$.

15. $333\frac{1}{3}$; through $(7{\cdot}94, 0)$. 17. $\frac{dA}{dx}=5x-x^2$; 12 sq.ft./sec.

18. At $x=1$; 1; $\left(x-\frac{1}{x^2}\right)v$.

Exercise 5*g*

1.51. 1. $2\pi ab^2$. 2. $50\pi a^3$.

3. $\pi c^2(b-a)-\frac{1}{3}\pi(b^3-a^3)$; $a=0$, $b=c$; $\frac{2}{3}\pi c^3$.

1.52. 4. $\frac{4}{3}\pi a^3$. 5. 36π cu.in. 6. $\frac{8}{3}\pi$.

7. $\frac{4}{3}\pi ab^2$. 8. $\pi\left(\frac{1}{a}-\frac{1}{b}\right)$; $\pi\frac{1}{a}$. 9. $\frac{29}{6}\pi a^3$.

PAGE

1.52. 10. $\frac{1}{6}\pi a^3$. 11. $0{\cdot}1215\pi = 0{\cdot}3817$ cu.cm.

1.53. 13. $\frac{125}{12}\pi$. 14. $\frac{16}{5}\pi$. 15. 4π.

17. $\frac{1}{2}\pi$. 18. $236\frac{2}{3}$ cu.in. 19. $180\frac{5}{9}$ gal.

20. 100 ft.; 100 million cu.ft.

CHAPTER 6

1.55. Ex. 1. (i) 5, (ii), 13, (iii) 25.

1.56. Ex. 3. (i) $(3, 3\frac{1}{2})$, (ii) $(\frac{1}{2}, -5)$, (iii) $(2\frac{1}{2}, 2\frac{1}{2})$.

1.57. Ex. 5. (i) $(3\frac{4}{5}, 7\frac{4}{5})$, (ii) $(-\frac{4}{9}, \frac{1}{9})$, (iii) $\left(\dfrac{4x_1+5x_2}{9}, \dfrac{4y_1+5y_2}{9}\right)$.

Ex. 6. (i) (8, 6), (ii) (0, 9), (iii) $(5x_2-4x_1, 5y_2-4y_1)$.

1.58. Ex. 7. (i) 2, (ii) 1, (iii) $-\frac{2}{3}$, (iv) $\frac{1}{2}$, (v) 0, (vi) ∞.

Ex. 9. (i) $x-2y+5=0$, (ii) $x+y+1=0$, (iii) $2x-y=12$, (iv) $3x+4y=11$.

1.59. Ex. 11. (i) $2x-y=4$, (ii) $x-y=1$, (iii) $2x+3y=5$, (iv) $x=2y$, (v) $y=2$, (vi) $x=3$.

Ex. 12. (i) $3x-y=7$, (ii) $4x+3y+5=0$, (iii) $x-y=0$.

1.60. Ex. 14. (i) $x+3y=6$, (ii) $3x-4y+11=0$, (iii) $x+y=0$.

Ex. 16. (i) $4x+3y=33$, (ii) (6, 3), (iii) 5.

Ex. 17. (i) $(11\frac{1}{3}, 7)$, $8\frac{1}{3}$, (ii) $\frac{3}{4}$, $\frac{3}{5}$, (iii) 5.

Ex. 18. (i) 5, (ii) 1, (iii) $\frac{1}{2}\sqrt{2}$, (iv) 3.

1.61. Ex. 19. (i) $16x-y=22$, $x+16y=162$; (ii) $3x-y=5$, $x+3y=25$, (iii) $3x+4y=24$, $4x-3y=7$, (iv) $7x-2y+28=0$, $2x+7y=45$.

1.62. Ex. 20. $x^2+y^2=25$, $3x+4y=25$, $4x=3y$.

Ex. 21. $x^2+y^2+6x-8y=0$; tangents $3x-4y=0$, $3x+4y=32$; normals $4x+3y=0$, $4x-3y+24=0$.

Ex. 22. $(x-a)^2+(y-b)^2=r^2$.

Ex. 23. (i) (1, 4), 3; (ii) $(-3, 2)$, 1.

Ex. 24. Tangents $3x+4y=36$, $3x-4y=20$; normals $4x-3y+2=0$, $4x-3y=0$.

1.64. Ex. 27. S-symmetry (i), (ii), (iv), (vi); (iii) and (vi) about $x=0$; (iv) about both axes.

1.65. Ex. 29. (i) $x=3$, $(3, -4)$, (ii) $x=-\frac{1}{2}$, $(-\frac{1}{2}, 3\frac{1}{4})$, (iii) $x=2$, $(2, -4)$, (iv) $x=-1$, $(-1, 2)$.

1.66. Ex. 30. (i) $x=2$, $y=3$, (ii) $x=-1$, $y=2$.

1.67. Ex. 31. 6, 4.

Exercise 6*a*

PAGE

1.69. 1. At A, $(1\frac{1}{2}, 1\frac{1}{2})$.

2. (i) $(-5, 3)$, $(-4, 2)$, (ii) $x+y+2=0$, $x+y=2$, (iii) $x-y+8=0$.

3. $(-3, 1)$, $(-10, -3)$; $\frac{1}{6}$, 3.

4. (i) $2x-y+1=0$, (ii) $x+2y=7$, (iii) $(-1, 4)$, $\sqrt{5}$.

5. $4\frac{1}{12}$, $2x-3y=0$. 6. $6\frac{1}{2}$.

7. (i) $x+2y-7=0$, (ii) $3x-2y+11=0$, (iii) $20x+3y=0$.

8. $2x-5y+17=0$; $(4, 5)$, $(-6, 1)$.

1.70. 9. $9x+y=32$, $3x-5y+32=0$, $y=3x$; $(2\frac{2}{3}, 8)$.

10. 1; $x^2+y^2+2x-6y+9=0$.

11. $x-3y+1=0$, $5x-2y+5=0$, $4x+y=22$.

12. 19. 13. $y=7$, $3x-y=1$; No.

14. 1, -1; $x-y+1=0$, $4x+4y=11$.

15. $x+8ty=16t^2+t$; $(0, 2t+\frac{1}{8})$.

16. (i) $(-1, 5)$, $(3, 24)$, (ii) $(1, 5)$. A tangent.

17. -1, $(1, 2)$. 18. ± 1, $x\mp y+2=0$.

19. $x+t^2y=2t$. 20. $8k$, $-4k$, $8k$; $\pm\frac{1}{8}\sqrt{2}$.

1.71. 21. $x+2y=12$; $(-6, 9)$. 22. $(1, 4)$, $(3, 12)$.

23. $3x+4y=\pm 36$; $(6, 4\frac{1}{2})$, $(-6, -4\frac{1}{2})$.

24. $-\frac{1}{4}$; -5, 8. 25. $(2, 6\frac{1}{2})$; $x-4y=1$.

26. $3x+y=5$, $(\frac{1}{2}, 3\frac{1}{2})$. 27. $(3, -2)$, 5; $4x+3y=6$; $(0, 2)$.

28. $y^2=4x$; $(9, 6)$, $(1, -2)$. At $(1, -2)$.

30. $x^2+y^2-6x+18y+85=0$. 31. $(1, 7)$, 5.

1.72. 32. $(\frac{1}{2}a, \frac{1}{2}b)$, $xy=c^2$. 33. $(2, 4)$, $(1+\sqrt{5}, 2)$.

34. $4x^2+4y^2+ax+ay=a^2$; $\frac{3}{8}a\sqrt{2}$, $(-\frac{1}{8}a, -\frac{1}{8}a)$.

35. $x^2+y^2-4x-2y=0$; $(0, 0)$, $(4, 2)$.

CHAPTER 7

(Constants have been omitted from answers to indefinite integrals)

1.75. Ex. 5. (i) $2\sqrt{x}$. (ii) $-x^{-1}$. (iii) $-\dfrac{1}{2x^2}$. (iv) $2\sqrt{x^5}$. (v) $6\sqrt[3]{x^4}$.

1.77. Ex. 8. 32.

Exercise 7*a*

1. $5x^4$. 2. $8x^3-10x$. 3. $3x^2-\dfrac{2}{x^2}$.

4. $10x^9-30x^5$. 5. $12(3x-5)^3$. 6. $-20(1-2x)^9$.

7. $-4(4x-1)^{-2}$. 8. $na(ax+b)^{n-1}$. 9. $6x(x^2+1)^2$.

10. $24x(3x^2-5)^3$. 11. $-18x^2(4-3x^3)$. 12. $-3ndx^2(c-dx^3)^{n-1}$.

PAGE

1.78. 13. $\frac{1}{\sqrt{(2x+3)}}$. 14. $-\frac{15}{2}(4-5x)^{\frac{1}{2}}$. 15. $\frac{1}{2(2-x)^{\frac{3}{2}}}$.

16. $-\frac{3}{2}b(a-bx)^{\frac{1}{2}}$. 17. $\frac{2}{3}x(x^2-1)^{-\frac{2}{3}}$. 18. $-2x^2(2x^3+3)^{-\frac{4}{3}}$.

19. $2(x-x^3)(x^4-2x^2)^{-\frac{3}{2}}$. 20. $nrx^{n-1}(x^n+1)^{r-1}$. 21. $50(5x-1)^9$.

22. $4x^3+\frac{2}{x^3}$. 23. $3\left(1+\frac{1}{x^2}\right)\left(x-\frac{1}{x}\right)^2$. 24. $-\frac{6}{(3x-5)^3}$.

25. $-\frac{1}{2}\sqrt{\frac{2}{x^3}}$. 26. $3x\sqrt{(x^2-1)}$. 27. $-\frac{1}{2}(4x-1)(2x^2-x)^{-\frac{3}{2}}$

28. $60x^2(4x^3+1)^4$. 29. $8ax(ax^2-b)^3$. 30. $-\frac{1}{2}a^2(ax+b)^{-\frac{3}{2}}$.

31. $2nax(ax^2+b)^{n-1}$. 32. $-n(2ax+b)(ax^2+bx+c)^{-n-1}$.

33. $\frac{1}{2}x^4-\frac{1}{2}x^2$. 34. $\frac{4}{3}x^3+5x$. 35. $2x+\frac{1}{x}$.

36. $x^2-\frac{3}{x}$. 37. $\frac{1}{8}(2x-3)^4$. 38. $-\frac{1}{18}(1-3x)^6$.

39. $\frac{1}{5}(1-5x)^{-1}$. 40. $-\frac{1}{a(n-1)}(ax+b)^{-n+1}$. 41. $\sqrt{(2x+3)}$.

42. $\frac{3}{4}(x-5)^{\frac{4}{3}}$. 43. $\frac{2}{15}(3x+2)^{\frac{5}{2}}$. 44. $\frac{3}{25}(2-5x)^{-\frac{5}{3}}$.

45. $\frac{2}{9}(3x-4)^{\frac{3}{2}}$. 46. $\frac{1}{33}(3x-4)^{11}$. 47. $-\frac{1}{28}(2-7x)^4$.

48. $\frac{3}{20}(3+5x)^{\frac{4}{3}}$. 49. $\frac{2}{3}x^{\frac{3}{2}}-x$. 50. $-\frac{1}{4(2x-5)^2}$.

51. $\frac{4}{9}(3x-4)^{\frac{3}{4}}$. 52. $2\sqrt{x}+\frac{1}{3x^3}$. 53. $\sqrt{(x^2+1)}$.

54. $\frac{2}{9}(x^3-2)^{\frac{3}{2}}$. 55. $\frac{1}{15}(x^{10}+1)^{\frac{3}{2}}$. 56. $\frac{1}{9}(3x^2-4)^{\frac{3}{2}}$.

57. $-\frac{5}{2}$. 58. (1, 2). 59. $\frac{1}{\sqrt{3}}$.

60. 1. 61. 5 ft./sec.^{2} 62. ± 200 ft./sec.^{2}

1.79. Ex. 10. $3x^2-10x+3$.

Ex. 11. (i) $x(x-1)^2(5x-2)$. (ii) $\frac{3x+2}{2\sqrt{(x+1)}}$.

(iii) $(x+1)^2(x-1)(5x-1)$. (iv) $\frac{x-3}{x^2}\sqrt{(2x+3)}$.

1.81. Ex. 12. (i) $\frac{13}{(3x+2)^2}$. (ii) $\frac{34}{(3-5x)^2}$. (iii) $\frac{x^2-2x-1}{(x-1)^2}$.

(iv) $\frac{3(1-x^2)}{(x^2+1)^2}$. (v) $-\frac{3x^2+2}{2(x^2-2)^2\sqrt{x}}$. (vi) $\frac{3-2x}{2x^2\sqrt{x}}$.

Ex. 13. $\frac{2(7-3x)}{(3x-4)^4}$.

Ex. 14. $\frac{1}{2\sqrt{x}}$; $2y$; yes.

Ex. 15. $\frac{1}{6x^{\frac{2}{3}}}$; $24y^2$; yes.

PAGE

1.82. Ex. 16. (i) $\dfrac{1}{6x+1}$. (ii) $\dfrac{x^2}{x^2-1}$.

1.85. Ex. 17. (i) $\dfrac{1}{t}$. (ii) $\dfrac{2t}{1+t^2}$.

Ex. 18. (i) $\dfrac{1}{2t^3}$. (ii) $-\dfrac{2}{9t^4}$. (iii) $\dfrac{3}{16t^5}$.

Exercise 7*b*

1.86. 1. $(x-4)^3(5x-4)$. 2. $6(3x-1)(5-2x)^2(6-5x)$.

3. $nx^{n-1}(a-x)^{n-1}(a-2x)$. 4. $\dfrac{3x+2}{2\sqrt{x}}$. 5. $\dfrac{12x^2+4x+3}{\sqrt{(2x^2+1)}}$.

6. $-\dfrac{x}{\sqrt{(1-x^2)}}$. 7. $\dfrac{2}{(x+2)^2}$. 8. $\dfrac{25}{(3x+4)^2}$.

9. $\dfrac{bc+ad}{(c-dx)^2}$. 10. $\dfrac{x-1}{2x\sqrt{x}}$. 11. $\dfrac{1}{x^2\sqrt{(x^2-1)}}$.

12. $-\dfrac{1}{x^2\sqrt{(ax^2+b)}}$. 13. $(x-5)(x+6)^2(5x-3)$. 14. $\dfrac{6(3x-5)(8-x)}{(2x+3)^4}$

15. $\dfrac{1}{\sqrt{\{x(x+2)^3\}}}$. 16. $\dfrac{3(2-x)}{x^3\sqrt{(2x-3)}}$. 17. $\dfrac{-3(2x+1)}{(x-1)^2(x+2)^2}$.

18. $-\dfrac{3(2x^3-x^2-3)}{(x^3+3)^2}$. 19. $-\dfrac{3}{5x^2\sqrt{(2x^2+3)}}$.

20. $-\dfrac{3(9x^2-x+4)}{\sqrt{\{(4+3x^2)(1-6x)\}}}$. 21. $-\dfrac{2x^2+1}{x^2(x^2+1)^{\frac{3}{2}}}$.

22. $6(3x-5)(2x+1)^2(5x-4)$. 23. $\dfrac{30x^2-5x+6}{\sqrt{(5x^2+2)}}$.

24. $\dfrac{x(11-4x^2)}{\sqrt{\{(2x^2-3)(4-x^2)\}}}$. 25. $\dfrac{6x(5-7x+x^3)}{(7-3x^2)^2}$.

26. $\dfrac{5}{2\sqrt{\{(x+2)^3(2x-1)\}}}$. 27. $\dfrac{3(4x^2-1)}{x^4\sqrt{(1-3x^2)^3}}$.

28. $36x^2-4$; $72x$. 29. $90x^8$; $720x^7$. 30. $30x^{\frac{1}{2}}$; $15x^{-\frac{1}{2}}$.

31. $10(x^2+1)^3(9x^2+1)$. 32. $-\dfrac{3x}{(x^2+1)^{\frac{5}{2}}}$. 33. $-\dfrac{a^2}{y^3}$.

34. $\frac{3}{2}t$; $\dfrac{3}{4t}$. 35. $\dfrac{1}{t(2+t)}$; $-\dfrac{2(1+t)^3}{t^3(2+t)^3}$.

36. $\dfrac{t(2-t^3)}{1-2t^3}$; $\dfrac{2(t^3+1)^4}{(1-2t^3)^4}$. 37. $\dfrac{(t^2-1)}{2t}$; $-\dfrac{(1+t^2)^3}{8t^3}$.

PAGE

1.87. 39. $-\frac{11}{2}$, 7. **40.** (i) $t=\frac{7}{4}$, (ii) $t=\frac{1}{2}$ and 3.

42. $\dfrac{2+3t^2}{2t+3}$; $\dfrac{2(3t^2+9t-2)}{(2t+3)^3}$. **43.** $\frac{1}{2}$, max.

45. $\dfrac{t^2+1}{t^2-1}$; $(2a, 0)$, $(-2a, 0)$; $\dfrac{-4t^3}{a(t^2-1)^3}$.

47. (i) $\dfrac{1}{\sqrt{2}}$, (ii) $-\dfrac{1}{\sqrt{2}}$. 48. $-\dfrac{x+y}{x+3y}$.

Exercise 8*a*

1.91. 1. (i) $\frac{1}{3}x^3+x^2+3x$. (ii) $-\dfrac{2}{x}-5x$. (iii) $\frac{5}{3}x^3-\frac{3}{2}x^2+7x$.

(iv) $\frac{2}{3}(x-5)^{\frac{3}{2}}$. (v) $\frac{1}{9}(3x+2)^3$. (vi) $-\frac{1}{5}(7-2x)^{\frac{5}{2}}$.

2. (i) 16. (ii) 7. (iii) 14. (iv) 21. (v) 9. (vi) 0.

3. (i) 4. (ii) 26. (iii) $4\frac{1}{2}$. (iv) 33. (v) 0. (vi) $18\frac{2}{3}$. (vii) $5\frac{1}{3}-\frac{4}{3}\sqrt{2}$. (viii) 68. (ix) 2.

1.92. Ex. 2. $\dfrac{k^3}{12a}$; $\frac{4}{3}h\sqrt{(ah)}=\frac{2}{3}hk$.

1.93. Ex. 4. $41\frac{2}{3}$.

Exercise 8*b*

1. 37.

1.94. 2. 2. 3. $4\frac{2}{3}$. 4. $1\frac{1}{3}$. 5. 64.

6. $2\frac{2}{3}$. 7. $\frac{1}{6}$. 8. $6\frac{1}{6}$. 9. $3\frac{1}{3}$.

10. 44. 11. 3. 12. $12\frac{2}{3}$. 13. $1\frac{1}{3}$.

14. $4\frac{1}{2}$. 15. $5\frac{1}{3}$; $10\frac{2}{3}$. 16. $5\frac{1}{3}$. 17. $1\frac{1}{3}$.

18. $2\frac{2}{3}$. 19. $\frac{4}{7}$. 20. $2\frac{2}{3}$. 21. $4\frac{1}{2}$.

1.95. 22. $2\frac{2}{3}$. 23. (i) $1\frac{1}{3}$, (ii) $6\frac{2}{3}$. 24. $\frac{1}{3}$. 25. $\frac{2}{21}a^2$.

1.96. Ex. 5. 7.

Exercise 8*c*

1. (i) $12\frac{1}{2}$, (ii) $-12\frac{1}{2}$, (iii) 0. 2. (i) -24, (ii) 24, (iii) 0.

3. (i) $11\frac{1}{3}$, (ii) $3\frac{1}{3}$. 4. (i) $18\frac{2}{3}$, (ii) $2\frac{2}{3}$.

5. (i) -9, (ii) $-10\frac{2}{3}$. 6. (i) $10\frac{3}{4}$, (ii) $11\frac{1}{4}$.

7. (i) $-5\frac{1}{3}$, (ii) $-10\frac{2}{3}$, (iii) 0. 8. 3, $\frac{3}{4}$.

9. (i) 4, (ii) 0. 10. 4, 4. 11. $6\frac{3}{4}$.

1.98. Ex. 9. $2\pi ab^2$.

Exercise 8*d*

1. 8π. 2. $\frac{5}{24}\pi$. 3. $\frac{24}{35}\pi$.

4. $\frac{128}{5}\pi$ cu.in. 5. $\frac{1}{6}\pi a^3$. 6. 243π cu.in.

7. (i) $2\pi a^3$, (ii) $4\pi a^3$. 8. $h^2(a-\frac{2}{3}h)$. 9. $\frac{16}{5}\pi$.

10. $\frac{8}{5}\pi$.

PAGE

1.99. 11. $\frac{27}{32}$; 6π c.c. 13. $32\frac{1}{2}\pi$; $168\frac{4}{5}\pi$. 14. 2π.
15. 6 and 7. 16. $\frac{1}{24}\pi$. 17. $\frac{3}{10}\pi$.
18. $85\frac{1}{3}\pi$. 19. $81\frac{1}{15}\pi$.

1.100. Ex. 10. 5.
Ex. 11. $2\frac{8}{15}$.
Ex. 12. 2.

Exercise 8*e*

1.101. 1. (i) 1, (ii) $1\frac{1}{3}$, (iii) 2. 2. 11. 3. (i) 64 ft./sec., (ii) $85\frac{1}{3}$ ft./sec.

1.102. 4. $\frac{2}{3}\pi a^2$. 5. $\frac{1}{3}\pi a^2$.
6. 2·37 gm.wt./sq.cm. 7. $\frac{1}{3}(a^2+ab+b^2)$.
8. (i) $21\frac{2}{3}\pi$, (ii) $21\frac{2}{3}\pi$. 9. (i) $u-\frac{1}{2}gt$, (ii) $\frac{2}{3}u$.
10. (i) $36\frac{1}{4}$ ft., (ii) $56\frac{2}{3}$ ft.
11. $y_2, \dfrac{y_3-y_1}{2h}, \dfrac{y_1-2y_2+y_3}{2h^2}$; $\frac{1}{6}(y_1+4y_2+y_3)$.

INDEX